OXFORD STUDIES
IN
NUCLEAR PHYSICS

GENERAL EDITOR
P. E. HODGSON

SYMMETRY PRINCIPLES IN PARTICLE PHYSICS

J. McL. Emmerson

CLARENDON PRESS · OXFORD

1972

Oxford University Press, Ely House, London W.1

GLASGOW   NEW YORK   TORONTO   MELBOURNE   WELLINGTON
CAPE TOWN   IBADAN   NAIROBI   DAR ES SALAAM   LUSAKA   ADDIS ABABA
DELHI   BOMBAY   CALCUTTA   MADRAS   KARACHI   LAHORE   DACCA
KUALA LUMPUR   SINGAPORE   HONG KONG   TOKYO

PRINTED IN GREAT BRITAIN
BY J. W. ARROWSMITH LTD.,
BRISTOL 3

TO

S.J.M.

PREFACE

THE idea of symmetry has always played an important part in physical theory. It is used to simplify concepts, clarify discussions, and give added elegance to formal proofs. However in particle physics its role is specially important. For in particle physics much of our present dynamical theory is incomplete or unsatisfactory and it is reasonable to hope that many of the ideas and models will be discarded or radically modified by the end of the century. In contrast, the results derived from symmetry theory are believed to be of much more permanent value. They are not a substitute for detailed dynamics, but they provide constraints which apply to any dynamical theory and their predictions can be explored and tested long before the details of such a theory have been worked out. Taken collectively, they provide a framework into which any subsequent theory must fit and in terms of which one can classify and interpret the present mass of experimental data. Thus in particle physics symmetry theory offers much more than just a set, however elegant, of insights and short cuts. It forms much of the basis on which the whole subject is built.

The present book is an attempt to give a unified treatment of symmetry theory independent of any specific dynamical models. It is concerned with the transformations which can be applied to a system and still leave the physics of that system unchanged (symmetry principles) and with the conditions under which certain observables remain constant with time (conservation laws). It considers their nature and most general properties and the relationship between them. The various principles are considered roughly in order of increasing complexity. Where a single principle leads to a variety of consequences, these consequences are enumerated and classified. Much stress is laid on the unity of symmetry theory and a unified formalism is used throughout. The book allows the student to examine symmetry ideas before coming to grips with detailed experimental data. It therefore concentrates exclusively on these ideas and makes no attempt to examine all, or even the most important, experimental applications. The ideas are illustrated by detailed discussions of a small number of examples, but other equally important examples are omitted entirely. However with this theoretical framework the reader should be able to see more clearly the essential value and limitations of the various experiments which he will find described in the literature.

The book is written specifically as a text book for research students in nuclear and particle physics, but it is hoped that it will also be of use to final year undergraduates and to the younger research workers who want to think more carefully about some of the statements they find in the literature. It assumes a knowledge of undergraduate particle physics and a thorough grounding in elementary quantum mechanics. Without the former, the motives for introducing the various principles will be difficult to understand and without the latter much of the formalism will be obscure. Some preliminary reading in one of the more general introductions to symmetry principles (e.g. Weyl 1952, or Wigner 1967) would also be helpful. The book assumes little mathematics. A basic grasp of matrix algebra is essential, but otherwise any necessary algebra is developed in the text. The elementary tensor algebra needed for discussing SU_3 and SU_6, for instance, is all developed before these topics are introduced. However, while the whole emphasis of the book is on physical ideas rather than formal mathematical development, it is important at this level that proofs should be given and the basic mathematics thoroughly understood.

A special word is needed about group theory. The language of group theory is a natural one for discussing symmetry principles. However most physicists begin graduate work without it and I have found that any attempt to explain it at the beginning of a short course on symmetry principles means that the essential physics is obscured by the formalism. For this reason, the book assumes no knowledge of group theory and as far as possible avoids all group theoretical language. This necessarily involves some compromise, but this compromise is essential for experimental physicists and in practice the younger theoreticians also gain useful insights from this alternative approach.

The book has been kept short and it is hoped that the student will work straight through it. Chapter 1 serves two purposes. First, it reviews the basic quantum mechanics and matrix algebra which will be needed in the rest of the book. This will be familiar to most readers, but a little revision is usually helpful and it also serves to establish some of the essential formalism for later chapters. Secondly, it gives a very general and largely elementary introduction to symmetry and invariance principles and the relationship between the two. This provides the framework for all subsequent discussions and it is essential that it be clearly understood. The notation introduced in this chapter is followed throughout the book. Thus, for instance, R always denotes an observable, T a symmetry operator, H the Hamiltonian, and so on.

The subsequent sections consider most of the important symmetry principles in turn, the principal omissions being the Lorentz transformation and certain selection rules for the weak interactions. The discussion usually begins with a simple physical idea and then uses the methods of Chapter 1 to explore its consequences. The formalism, predictions, and validity of each principle are discussed, and as far as possible proofs are given in detail. Chapter 2 deals with the discrete symmetries, parity, charge conjugation, and time reversal, and with two combined operations, PC and PCT. It emphasizes that all these principles are primarily symmetry principles and that the usual relationship derived in Chapter 1 between symmetry principles and conservation laws does not apply. The predictions from these principles are very varied and the connections between them are explored in detail. Chapter 3 deals with the superselection rules which can be derived when a physical observable is strictly conserved in all possible interactions. It concentrates mainly on the differences between superselection and ordinary selection rules, and on the difficulties raised by the former for the concepts of intrinsic space- and charge-parity. Chapter 4 deals with angular momentum and isospin. It develops the algebra of angular momentum starting with the generators of infinitesimal rotations and then goes on to show the connection between this and the algebra of SU_2. The necessary tensor formalism is given in detail. It is then easy to discuss intrinsic spin and isospin and to explore their physical consequences. Finally the results are used to discuss the G-parity and time reversal operators. Chapter 5 deals with SU_3 and relies heavily on the tensor algebra introduced in the previous chapter. SU_3 is used to classify states and predict their quantum numbers. Where its predictions do not agree with experiment the reasons are discussed in detail. The latter part of the chapter introduces the concept of a broken symmetry and shows that many of the more interesting results from SU_3 can be derived precisely because the symmetry is not exact. The final chapter deals with SU_6. It shows how SU_6 can be used to classify states with the help of the algebra developed in earlier chapters. However, since SU_6 is much less important than SU_3, the argument is less detailed and the reader is referred to other texts for more advanced discussions.

In deciding how much detail to give, I have been strongly influenced by the questions asked by successive research students. Why are final-state interactions relevant in tests of time reversal, but not of parity? If parity and momentum are both conserved in the strong interaction, why do the corresponding operators not commute? Why do parity and charge conjugation lead to conservation laws while time reversal does not? How much of the usual discussion of G-parity depends on phase conventions? Why is the SU_2 rank-two singlet written in an anti-symmetric form while the SU_3 rank-two singlet is symmetric? These and many other similar questions are not purely formal. They indicate a concern for the foundations of symmetry theory and one's understanding is enormously strengthened by thinking through the answers.

    References are given in all chapters, but the number has deliberately been kept small since most research students find over-extensive bibliographies both confusing and discouraging. References are given to original papers for experiments discussed in the text. However, since the book is an attempt to present fundamental ideas rather than to review 'the state of the art', a detailed bibliography of the more controversial experimental questions would be out of place. References are therefore given to texts or papers containing reviews of the literature. Equally, since the book does not aim to list the experimental applications of symmetry principles, many important experiments are cited only indirectly through review articles. Thus the bibliography is not only rather short, but it also consists mainly of secondary sources. Amongst these sources, however, will be found useful bibliographies covering all aspects of symmetry principles and their applications. When choosing between several texts and reviews, I have usually simply cited those which seem to be most popular in practice. In particular, I have made extensive use of the excellent CERN summer school series which is widely available and written at exactly the right level.

    I should like to express my gratitude to the many Oxford research students whose stimulating discussions and comments have contributed so much to the flavour and content of the book; to Drs. I. J. R. Aitchison, P. E. Hodgson, and T. W. Quirk for reading the typescript and making detailed and very helpful suggestions; and lastly to the Warden and Fellows of New College for their constant interest and encouragement throughout the time when the book was being planned and written.

J. McL. E.

New College, Oxford
September 1971

CONTENTS

1

SYMMETRY AND CONSERVATION PRINCIPLES

BEFORE discussing the various principles individually, it is necessary
to consider just what a symmetry principle is and how it fits into the
framework of quantum mechanics. The present chapter is intended to
provide an introduction to the ideas used in the rest of the book.
The first sections summarize some elementary results in quantum
mechanics and matrix algebra. They are included for revision and for
convenient reference later. If any of the material is unfamiliar, the
reader is advised to go first to the standard literature. The later sections
are devoted explicitly to symmetry and conservation principles.
First, it is shown that their definitions impose some important restrictions on the operators which can represent them. Some algebraic
consequences of this are developed and it is shown that the two types
of principle are not independent. In fact, every conservation law
implies a corresponding symmetry principle and it is often simply
convenience which dictates which of the two is used. The physical
content is the same for both.

1.1. State functions, observables, and transition probabilities

In quantum mechanics, all information about a physical system is
contained in its *state function*, ψ. This is a function of one or several
variables, the range of the variables depending on the individual
problem. The state function may have one or several components; that
is, more than one number may be needed to specify its value at any
point. Later chapters include examples of state functions represented
by scalars, vectors, and tensors of higher rank. However, each component can have only one value at any given point in space.
Furthermore, each component must be finite and the square of its
magnitude integrated over all space must also be finite.

State functions are given physical meaning by introducing observables. In quantum mechanics, every observable corresponds to a linear
operator and a measurement of the observable must always give a
value which occurs as an eigenvalue of the operator

$$R\psi_j = r_j\psi_j. \tag{1.1}$$

The notation here is conventional. R is the operator, r_j its jth eigenvalue and ψ_j the corresponding eigenfunction. The word *linear* means that R satisfies

$$R(\alpha\phi+\beta\chi) = \alpha R\phi+\beta R\chi \qquad (1.2)$$

for all states ϕ, χ and complex numbers α, β. A state function, ψ, can sometimes be expressed as the product of two other state functions, ϕ, χ, say. In this case

$$R\psi = \chi(R\phi)+\phi(R\chi). \qquad (1.2a)$$

If ϕ, χ are both eigenstates of R, then the eigenvalue of ψ will be the *sum* of the eigenvalues of ϕ, χ. For an arbitrary state function, ϕ, the *expectation value* of r (i.e. the mean results of a set of measurements of r) is

$$\langle r \rangle = \langle \phi|R|\phi \rangle / \langle \phi|\phi \rangle. \qquad (1.3)$$

The notation is again conventional. The right hand side is a convenient way to write

$$\sum \int \phi^*R\phi \, \mathrm{d}\tau \Big/ \sum \int \phi^*\phi \, \mathrm{d}\tau, \qquad (1.4)$$

where the integral is taken over the whole range of variables needed to describe ϕ and the summation over all components of ϕ^*, ϕ.

Two further postulates are needed to complete the picture. The first is the *principle of superposition*. This states that, if ϕ, χ are any two possible state functions for a system, then

$$\psi = \alpha\phi+\beta\chi \qquad (1.5)$$

is another possible state function for the system, where α, β are any two complex numbers. The properties of ψ can now be determined using eqns (1.2), (1.3). The second postulate states that the *transition probability* between any two states, ϕ, χ (i.e. the probability that a state ϕ will at a later time be found in the state χ) is

$$P = |\langle\chi|\phi\rangle|^2 / \langle\chi|\chi\rangle\langle\phi|\phi\rangle, \qquad (1.6)$$

where the vertical bars outside the angle brackets indicate, as usual, that the modulus is to be taken. In particular, the probability that a measurement of r made on a state, ϕ, will yield the eigenvalue, r_j, is given by

$$P = |\langle\psi_j|\phi\rangle|^2 / \langle\psi_j|\psi_j\rangle\langle\phi|\phi\rangle. \qquad (1.6a)$$

A state is taken to be defined by a set of numbers giving for each observable the relative probabilities that a given measurement will yield each of the possible eigenvalues.

These definitions and postulates have a number of important consequences. First note that nothing which has been said implies that we can determine unique values for the components of the state function at any point. We can make a set of measurements of an observable and hence determine its eigenvalues and its expectation value for any state. We can also measure the transition probability, P, between any two states. But that is all. Now it is immediately clear that if each state function is multiplied by an arbitrary complex number then neither the eigenvalues, r_j, nor the expectation values, $\langle r \rangle$, of any observable, R, will be changed. Furthermore, the transition probability, P, will be unchanged if ϕ is multiplied by an arbitrary complex number, α, and χ by another complex number, β, of arbitrary magnitude but the same phase as α. Consequently, any state function can be multiplied by an arbitrary real number without changing the physics and, while the *relative* phases of a set of state functions can sometimes be determined using transition probabilities, *absolute* phases cannot. Thus both the magnitude and the absolute phase of any state function can be chosen by convention. It is usual to adopt the convention that all state functions should be *normalized*

$$\langle \phi | \phi \rangle = 1. \tag{1.7}$$

It is important to remember that this is no more than a convention and that it has no physical content. It does, however, allow us to rewrite eqns (1.3), (1.6) in the simplified forms

$$\langle r \rangle = \langle \phi | R | \phi \rangle, \tag{1.8}$$

$$P = |\langle \chi | \phi \rangle|^2. \tag{1.9}$$

All state functions used in later sections are normalized unless the contrary is stated explicitly. Similarly, absolute phase can be chosen by convention, but this freedom has few advantages and will lead to a number of problems later. We shall meet further indeterminate properties of state functions when we come to consider symmetry principles.

A second consequence of the postulates of quantum mechanics is that, for any observable, R, the eigenstates corresponding to different eigenvalues are *orthogonal*. That is, if ψ_i, ψ_j are two eigenstates with eigenvalues r_i, r_j and $r_i \neq r_j$ then

$$\langle \psi_i | \psi_j \rangle = 0. \tag{1.10}$$

This is easily seen by considering the state function

$$\phi = \alpha \psi_i + \beta \psi_j, \tag{1.11}$$

where α, β are arbitrary complex numbers. Then the expectation value of r is

$$\langle r \rangle = \langle \alpha \psi_i + \beta \psi_j | R | \alpha \psi_i + \beta \psi_j \rangle$$

$$= |\alpha|^2 r_i + |\beta|^2 r_j + \beta^* \alpha \langle \psi_j | \psi_i \rangle r_i + \alpha^* \beta \langle \psi_i | \psi_j \rangle r_j \tag{1.12}$$

where we have used the facts that R is linear and that its eigenstates are normalized. But, since r_i, r_j, $\langle r \rangle$ are simply the numbers obtained from sets of measurements, their values must be *real*. Hence the imaginary part of the right hand side of eqn (1.12) must be zero;

$$\mathrm{Im}\{\beta^* \alpha \langle \psi_j | \psi_i \rangle r_i + (\beta^* \alpha \langle \psi_j | \psi_i \rangle)^* r_j\} = 0, \tag{1.13}$$

$$\therefore \quad \mathrm{Im}(\beta^* \alpha \langle \psi_j | \psi_i \rangle)(r_i - r_j) = 0. \tag{1.14}$$

Now, since $(r_i - r_j) \neq 0$ by hypothesis, and $\beta^* \alpha$ can be given any arbitrarily chosen phase, this condition can be satisfied only if ψ_i, ψ_j are orthogonal in accordance with (1.10). The result is proved.

Of course, one might ask what happens when several different eigenstates of R have the same eigenvalue. Will they still be orthogonal? The answer comes immediately by asking what one means by the phrase 'several different eigenstates'. If the phrase is to have any meaning, the states referred to must be definite states (that is eigenstates of one or more operators) but they must also be distinguishable. This implies that there must be at least one operator for which they do not have the same eigenvalues. Such states are said to be *degenerate* in R but not in the new operator. (Two states may, for instance, be degenerate in energy but not in angular momentum.) But, of course, if any such operator exists then the states must be orthogonal. One can therefore establish a set of mutually orthogonal states using the following procedure. Choose a set of operators which have the property that state functions can be simultaneously eigenstates of each member of the set. Then find all state functions which can be distinguished from each other through having different combinations of eigenvalues. Any two of these state functions will be orthogonal. We assume for convenience that the eigenvalues are discrete. The extension to the continuous case is straightforward.

The third consequence of the postulates of quantum mechanics is that this set of orthogonal state functions will also be *complete*. It is important to be clear about the meaning of this term. It implies that we have found state functions corresponding to all relevant combinations of eigenstates of our chosen set of operators. But it does not and obviously cannot imply that we will never find another operator which enables us to subdivide the set of state functions still further. It does not even rule out the possibility of an unexpected combination of eigenvalues within the chosen set. Rather it means that the set completely exhausts the combinations of eigenfunctions which are to be found in the problem under discussion. A further and most important implication is that any other state function which occurs in the problem can be expressed in one and only one way as a linear combination of members of the set. To see this, let ψ_j be our complete set of orthogonal normalized state functions (sometimes referred to as a complete *orthonormal* set) and let ϕ be another arbitrarily chosen normalized state function. Define a set of numbers

$$a_j \equiv \langle \psi_j | \phi \rangle. \tag{1.15}$$

Now, comparison with eqn (1.9) shows that $|a_j|^2$ gives the probability that, if ϕ is examined, it will be found to have the same eigenvalues as ψ_j. But the sum of these probabilities taken over all possible combinations of eigenvalues must be unity.

$$\therefore \quad \sum_j |a_j|^2 = 1. \tag{1.16}$$

It follows that

$$\langle \phi - \sum_j a_j \psi_j | \phi - \sum_j a_j \psi_j \rangle$$

$$= \langle \phi | \phi \rangle - \sum_j a_j \langle \phi | \psi_j \rangle - \sum_j a^*_j \langle \psi_j | \phi \rangle + \sum_j |a_j|^2 \tag{1.17}$$

$$= 2 - 2 \sum_j |a_j|^2 = 0.$$

$$\therefore \quad \phi = \sum_j a_j \psi_j. \tag{1.18}$$

Hence ϕ can be expressed as a linear combination of the ψ_j. It remains to show that this linear combination is unique. To see this, suppose

2PP

that there exists another set of coefficients, b_j say, such that

$$\phi = \sum_j a_j \psi_j = \sum_j b_j \psi_j. \tag{1.19}$$

Then

$$\langle \psi_i | \phi \rangle = \sum_j a_j \langle \psi_i | \psi_j \rangle = \sum_j b_j \langle \psi_i | \psi_j \rangle, \tag{1.20}$$

$$\therefore \quad a_i = b_i, \tag{1.21}$$

where we have used the fact that the ψ_j are orthonormal. Eqn (1.21) holds for all b_i and hence the result is proved. An immediate consequence of this is that the states, ψ_j, are *linearly independent*. That is, no one of them can be expressed as a linear combination of the others.

The existence of complete orthonormal sets of state functions simplifies the algebra of quantum mechanics considerably. If any state, ϕ, can be expressed in one and only one way in terms of n suitably chosen states, ψ_j, as in eqn (1.18), then it follows that it can be specified completely in terms of only n numbers—the a_j. The algebra of quantum mechanics can then be reduced to the algebra of the a_j. The n states, ψ_j, are called *basis states*. Now, there may of course be many possible sets of basis states. An alternative set, ψ'_i say, can always be established if there exists any observable, R', for which the ψ_j are not eigenstates. Each ψ_j can be expressed as a linear combination of the ψ'_i and vice versa.

$$\psi_j = \sum_i c_j^i \psi'_i, \tag{1.22}$$

$$\psi'_i = \sum_k d_k^i \psi_k. \tag{1.23}$$

However the number, n, of ψ_j must equal the number, m say, of ψ'_i. In order to see this, substitute eqn (1.23) into eqn (1.22).

$$\therefore \quad \psi_j = \sum_i \sum_k c_i^j d_k^i \psi_k \tag{1.24}$$

$$\therefore \quad \sum_i c_i^j d_k^i = \delta_k^j, \tag{1.25}$$

where

$$\delta_k^j = 1 \text{ for } j = k \tag{1.26}$$

$$= 0 \text{ otherwise.}$$

Now the total number, n, of ψ_j is given by

$$n = \sum_j \delta_j^j = \sum_j \sum_i c_i^j d_j^i. \tag{1.27}$$

But exactly the same expression gives the number, m, of ψ'_i and the result is proved. We conclude that, while the explicit choice of basis states can be made arbitrarily for convenience in solving a particular problem, the *number* of basis states is not arbitrary and is determined by the nature of the problem itself. It is called the *dimension* of the basis. Conversion from one set of basis states to another can be made using equations of the form (1.22). Suppose that a state, ϕ, is given by eqn (1.18) then

$$\phi = \sum_j a_j \psi_j = \sum_i \sum_j c_i^j a_j \psi'_i. \tag{1.28}$$

But this gives a new expansion of ϕ in terms of the ψ'_i.

$$\phi = \sum_i a'_i \psi'_i, \tag{1.29}$$

where

$$a'_i = \sum_j c_i^j a_j. \tag{1.30}$$

The a_j and a'_i describe the same state using two different bases. Now equations of the form (1.30) immediately suggest a convenient algebra for quantum mechanics. The expansion coefficients, a_j, can be treated as the elements of an n dimensional column vector known as a *state vector*. The a'_i are elements of another vector describing the same state but using a different basis. Clearly the c_i^j can likewise be considered as the elements of a *square matrix* describing the transition between bases. Eqn (1.30) gives the familiar rule for multiplying a vector by a matrix.

Now let R be any operator corresponding to an observable and let it have eigenfunctions ψ_j with eigenvalues r_j. Consider the function, $R\phi$, obtained by operating with R on ϕ. Since R is linear

$$R\phi = \sum_j a_j R\psi_j = \sum_j a_j r_j \psi_j. \tag{1.31}$$

$R\phi$ is a new state vector with elements b_j say, where

$$b_j = a_j r_j. \tag{1.32}$$

But suppose that it is necessary to use basis vectors, ψ'_i, which are not eigenstates of R. Then

$$R\phi = \sum_i \sum_j c_i^j r_j a_j \psi'_i. \tag{1.33}$$

$R\phi$ is still a state vector, but its elements are given by

$$b'_i = \sum_j c_i^j r_j a_j \tag{1.34}$$

$$\equiv \sum_j R_i^j a_j, \tag{1.35}$$

where the R^j are *numbers* defined by this equation. Once again, they can be considered as elements of a square matrix. Eqn (1.32) is obviously a special case of eqn (1.35) with

$$R_i^j = \delta_i^j r_j. \tag{1.36}$$

A matrix of this form is said to be *diagonal*.

To conclude: for any quantum mechanical problem, it is possible to choose a complete, orthogonal, normalized set of basis states. When this has been done, any other state function can be expressed as a vector in the space defined by the basis states and any observable can be expressed as a square matrix. Transition from one basis to another can also be effected using a square matrix. Clearly, then, matrix algebra is of fundamental importance in quantum mechanics. The next section lists some of its elementary features.

1.2. Matrices and determinants

This section summarizes some of the features of the algebra of square matrices. Many of the results will be used repeatedly in later sections. However the treatment is by no means complete and, if any of the results are unfamiliar, the reader should consult the standard literature (e.g. Margenau and Murphy 1961).

A matrix is a rectangular array of numbers and a *matrix element* is a number within the array. It is labelled by its position. Thus an element of a matrix, A, is written A_j^k where the lower index gives the row in which the element lies and the upper index gives the column. (Lower indices are said to be *covariant* and upper indices *contravariant*.) To every matrix there is an associated number called the *determinant*. This is defined by

$$|A| = \sum \epsilon(i, j, \ldots, l) A_1^i A_2^j \ldots A_n^l, \tag{1.37}$$

where the summation is taken over all possible values of i, j, etc. and ϵ is defined by

$\epsilon = 1$ for $i, j, \ldots, l = 1, 2, \ldots, n$ respectively or some *even* permutation of these numbers,

$\epsilon = -1$ for $i, j, \ldots, l = $ any *odd* permutation of these numbers,

$\epsilon = 0$ if any pair of $i, j, \ldots, l$ are equal.

From this definition it follows that if any two rows or any two columns of A are interchanged then the sign of $|A|$ is changed. Hence, if any two rows or any two columns of A are equal, then $|A| = 0$.

Two square matrices, A, B, of the same dimension may be multiplied together. The product, AB, is also a square matrix and its elements are defined by

$$(AB)^k_j = \sum_l A^l_j B^k_l. \tag{1.38}$$

Summations of this sort occur frequently in matrix and tensor algebra and it is usual to adopt the *summation convention* that, where any index occurs more than once in an expression, summation over that index is assumed. Thus eqn (1.38) can be rewritten

$$(AB)^k_j = A^l_j B^k_l. \tag{1.39}$$

Similarly, the product of a matrix and a vector can be written

$$V'_j = A^l_j V_l. \tag{1.40}$$

This convention simplifies the notation considerably and will be used throughout this book. The determinant of the product of two matrices is equal to the product of the determinants

$$|AB| = |A|\,|B|. \tag{1.41}$$

This can be proved using the definition of determinants.

An important consequence of eqn (1.39) is that matrix multiplication is not in general *commutative*. That is

$$AB \neq BA. \tag{1.42}$$

(There are, of course, important and interesting exceptions to this rule.) It follows trivially, however, from eqn (1.41) that

$$|AB| = |BA|. \tag{1.43}$$

It is next necessary to define some standard operations.

1. Inversion

The *inverse*, A^{-1}, of a matrix, A, is defined by

$$AA^{-1} = I, \tag{1.44}$$

where I is the unit matrix defined by

$$I^k_j = \delta^k_j. \tag{1.45}$$

When multiplied by any matrix, it leaves that matrix unchanged. It is therefore sometimes called the *identity operator*. It follows from

(1.41) that $|A^{-1}|$ is the reciprocal of $|A|$ and hence that a matrix, A, will possess an inverse only if its determinant is non-zero. It is also easy to see that any matrix will commute with its inverse. For, suppose that B is a matrix satisfying

$$BA = I, \tag{1.46}$$

then multiplying on the right by A^{-1} gives

$$BAA^{-1} = A^{-1}$$
$$\therefore \quad B = A^{-1} \tag{1.47}$$

and the result is proved. The inverse, $(AB)^{-1}$, of the matrix product, AB, is given by

$$(AB)^{-1} = B^{-1}A^{-1}. \tag{1.48}$$

2. Transposition

The *transpose*, $\widetilde{A}$, of A is defined by

$$(\widetilde{A})^k_j = A^j_k. \tag{1.49}$$

It is obtained from A by transposing the rows into columns and vice versa. The following results are easily proved.

$$|\widetilde{A}| = |A'|,$$
$$(\widetilde{AB}) = \widetilde{B}\widetilde{A}. \tag{1.50}$$

3. Complex conjugation

The *complex conjugate*, A^*, of A is obtained by replacing every element of A by its complex conjugate.

4. Hermitian conjugation

This consists of transposition followed by complex conjugation. Thus the *hermitian conjugate*, $A^\dagger$, of A is defined by

$$(A^\dagger)^k_j = A^{*j}_k. \tag{1.51}$$

Some simple consequences of this definition are

$$|A^\dagger| = |A|^*, \tag{1.52}$$

$$(AB)^\dagger = B^\dagger A^\dagger. \tag{1.53}$$

There are several special types of matrix which are of particular importance in quantum mechanics.

1. The diagonal matrix

This has all elements, A_j^k, zero unless $j = k$, that is, unless the element lies on the diagonal of the matrix. Any two diagonal matrices will commute and their product will also be a diagonal matrix.

2. The unitary matrix

This is defined by the equation

$$AA^\dagger = I, \tag{1.54}$$

where I is the identity operator defined by eqn (1.45). It is easy to see that the product of two unitary matrices will also be unitary. If all the elements of a unitary matrix are real, it is said to be *real orthogonal*.

3. The hermitian matrix

A matrix is said to be *hermitian* if it is equal to its own hermitian conjugate.

$$A = A^\dagger. \tag{1.55}$$

Finally, it is necessary to introduce the most common type of matrix transformation. This is the *similarity transformation*. A' is a similarity transform of A if it satisfies an equation of the form

$$A' = UAU^{-1}, \tag{1.56}$$

where U is unitary. This type of transformation has a number of interesting properties. First, eqn (1.43) implies that A, A' have equal determinants. Secondly, consider the transform of $A^\dagger$.

$$UA^\dagger U^{-1} = (UAU^{-1})^\dagger = A'^\dagger. \tag{1.57}$$

Comparison of eqns (1.56), (1.57) shows that A' is hermitian if and only if A is hermitian. Similarly, A' is unitary if and only if A is also unitary. Thirdly, if A is either hermitian or unitary then it is always possible to find a suitable unitary matrix, U, such that A' is diagonal. The procedure for finding U is somewhat cumbersome and will not be discussed here. It is described in most texts on matrix algebra (e.g. Margenau and Murphy 1961). For our present purposes, the important point is that U exists and can be found explicitly if necessary. Finally, all matrix equations remain true after a similarity transformation. For instance, if $AB = BA$, then $A'B' = B'A'$. We shall see that this property makes it possible to concentrate on the equations themselves rather than on the explicit form of the matrices. In the following sections, we shall meet with many examples of similarity transformations and these properties will be of the highest importance.

1.3. The matrix formulation of quantum mechanics

In Section 1.1, we developed the view that the physical content of quantum mechanics comprises (a) the eigenvalues of all relevant observables, (b) the relative probabilities that a given measurement will yield each of the possible eigenvalues, and (c) the transition probability between any pair of states. We then showed that, since the eigenfunctions of any observable form a complete orthonormal set of state functions, it is possible to use them as basis states and to express any other state function in terms of them. This led to the idea that any state can be expressed as a state vector, any observable as a square matrix, and that the transition from one basis to another can also be effected using a square matrix. Having now developed some elementary matrix algebra, we can express the physics of quantum mechanics in an explicit matrix form.

Suppose that a state function, ϕ, can be expressed as a linear combination of the basis states, ψ_j, using eqn (1.18). Then it can also be treated as a state vector, V, with elements given by

$$V_j = a_j. \tag{1.58}$$

Now if another state function, χ, has expansion coefficients, b_j, which form the elements of a state vector, U, then

$$\langle \chi | \phi \rangle = \sum_j \sum_k \langle b_j \psi_j | a_k \psi_k \rangle = \sum_j b^*_j a_j, \tag{1.59}$$

where we have used the fact that the basis states form a complete orthonormal set. Now, using the rules for vector multiplication, it is easy to see that the right hand side of eqn (1.59) is simply the inner or scalar product of V and $U^\dagger$.

$$\langle \chi | \phi \rangle = U^\dagger V. \tag{1.60}$$

Next, suppose that we want to transform to another set of basis states. Eqn (1.30) states that vectors in one basis can be transformed to vectors in another basis using a square matrix, C, with elements c_i^j

$$V' = CV, \tag{1.61}$$

and by eqn (1.53),

$$V'^\dagger = V^\dagger C^\dagger. \tag{1.62}$$

An important restriction follows immediately. Suppose that V, U represent the basis states ψ_i, ψ_j. Then the elements of V, U are

$$V_k = \delta_k^i, \qquad U_k = \delta_k^j. \tag{1.63}$$

Under the transformation, C, these state vectors will change to V', U'. But eqns (1.7), (1.10) state that

$$\langle \psi_j | \psi_i \rangle = \delta_j^i \tag{1.64}$$

for *any* choice of basis states. It follows that

$$U'^\dagger V' = U^\dagger C^\dagger C V = \delta_j^i$$

$$\therefore \quad \delta_j^k (C^\dagger C)_k^l \delta_l^i = \delta_j^i$$

$$\therefore \quad C^\dagger C = I, \tag{1.65}$$

where the last step is achieved by summing over k, l and using the definition, (1.45), of I. Hence C is unitary (cf. eqn (1.54)) and it follows that the transformation from one basis to another is a unitary transformation.

Now consider the behaviour of the more general inner product, (1.60), under a change of basis

$$\langle \chi' | \phi' \rangle = U^\dagger C^\dagger C V = U^\dagger V = \langle \chi | \phi \rangle. \tag{1.66}$$

Clearly, it is left unchanged. In fact, eqn (1.66) shows without restriction that the inner product of any two states is left unchanged by a unitary transformation. This makes it possible to give a more general definition than eqn (1.54) of a unitary operator. Clearly eqn (1.66) is a *necessary* condition which must be satisfied if C is unitary; but the derivation of eqn (1.65) shows that it is also a *sufficient* one. For this reason, a unitary transformation, C, is sometimes defined as a transformation such that for any state functions ϕ, χ

$$\langle C\chi | C\phi \rangle = \langle \chi | \phi \rangle. \tag{1.67}$$

This definition is important since it can be used even if C is not expressed as a matrix. It will be shown in Section 1.5 that, while almost all symmetry operators are unitary, it is often either inconvenient or impossible to express them as matrices.

So much for state functions. Now consider the operators, R, corresponding to observables. The eigenvalue equation (1.1) becomes a set of n homogeneous simultaneous equations where n is the dimension of the basis.

$$(R - \lambda I)V = 0. \tag{1.68}$$

Here R is a matrix, V a vector and λ, the eigenvalue, a number. The techniques for solving linear equations are familiar and will not be discussed here. One theorem only is required. This states that eqn (1.68) will have a solution if and only if

$$|R - \lambda I| = 0. \tag{1.69}$$

That is, the determinant of $(R - \lambda I)$ must be zero. The eigenvalues, λ, of a matrix, R, are thus the roots of eqn (1.69) which is called the *secular* or *characteristic* equation.

Consider the form that R must take in various possible bases. In the simplest case, the eigenfunctions of R itself form the basis states. In this case, eqn (1.36) states that R will be a diagonal matrix and that its elements will be equal to its eigenvalues. Thus the jth eigenvalue, λ say, will be equal to R_j^j. Clearly, this provides a solution for (1.69). The more general case can be treated by transforming to another set of basis states. Now this transformation must satisfy three conditions. The new vector, V', must be given by eqn (1.61). The eigenvalue equation must have the form (1.68) with the new operator, R', substituted for R. And the eigenvalues, λ, must be unchanged. These conditions can be fulfilled by multiplying eqn (1.68) on the left by C, yielding

$$(CRC^{-1} - \lambda I)CV = 0; \tag{1.70}$$

and this can be written

$$(R' - \lambda I)V' = 0 \tag{1.71}$$

where

$$R' = CRC^{-1}, \tag{1.72}$$

and V' is given by eqn (1.61). Since eqn (1.72) is derived directly from eqn (1.68), it follows immediately that the eigenvalues of R' are the same as those of R. But, since C is unitary, R' is just a similarity transform of R. Hence similarity transforms leave eigenvalues unchanged. This result can also be obtained directly by noting that the secular equation for R' is

$$|R' - \lambda I| = |C|\,|R - \lambda I|\,|C^{-1}| = 0, \tag{1.73}$$

$$\therefore \quad |R - \lambda I| = 0 \tag{1.74}$$

where we have used eqn (1.41). It follows that the explicit matrix form of R can be found for any basis provided that its eigenvalues and the transforming matrix, C, are known. Conversely, if the explicit matrix form of R is known for any basis, then its eigenvalues can be found by determining the unitary matrix, C, which renders it diagonal.

One further important consequence of eqn (1.72) can be derived by remembering that, since the operator, R, corresponds to an observable and its eigenvalues give the *numbers* obtained by individual measurements of this observable, these eigenvalues must be real. It follows that, in its own basis, R is real as well as diagonal. But such a matrix is clearly its own hermitian conjugate and hence is hermitian. Now it was shown at the end of Section 1.2 that any similarity transform of an hermitian matrix is also hermitian. Thus, if R corresponds to an observable, it has real eigenvalues and its matrix form in *any* basis is hermitian. Conversely, any hermitian matrix has real eigenvalues. Since the concept of an hermitian operator is an extremely useful one, it is desirable to find some definition of hermiticity which can be used even if R is not expressed as a matrix. This is easily done. Let ϕ, χ be any two states expressed by vectors V, U respectively. Then, if R is hermitian,

$$U^\dagger R^\dagger V = U^\dagger R V$$

$$\therefore \quad \langle R\chi | \phi \rangle = \langle \chi | R\phi \rangle. \tag{1.75}$$

Conversely, if eqn (1.75) holds for all pairs of states including the basis states defined by eqn (1.63), then

$$\delta_j^k (R^\dagger)_k^l \delta_l^i = \delta_j^k R_k^l \delta_l^i,$$

$$\therefore \quad (R^\dagger)_j^i = R_j^i, \tag{1.76}$$

where the last step is achieved by summing over all k, l. Eqn (1.76) holds for all i, j and hence R is hermitian. Eqn (1.75) is thus both a necessary and sufficient condition that R should be hermitian. It is therefore often taken as the *definition* of an *hermitian* operator.

In section 1.1, we mentioned sets of observables which have the property that state functions can be simultaneous eigenstates of each member of the set. These sets were then used to define the basis states. It is useful to consider the mathematical restrictions which apply to these sets. Consider any two observables, R_1, R_2 say. If all basis states are eigenstates of both R_1, R_2, then the corresponding matrices must both be diagonal. Now diagonal matrices commute with each other and so form an important exception to eqn (1.42)

$$R_1 R_2 - R_2 R_1 = 0. \tag{1.77}$$

Equations of the form (1.77) occur so frequently in quantum mechanics that the left hand side is often expressed as

$$[R_1, R_2] \equiv R_1 R_2 - R_2 R_1. \tag{1.78}$$

$[R_1, R_2]$ is called the *commutator* of R_1, R_2. Now it is easy to see that if eqn (1.77) is true for one basis, then it is true for any other basis.

$$[R'_1, R'_2] = 0, \tag{1.79}$$

where R'_1, R'_2 are obtained from R_1, R_2 by the transformation (1.72). Thus eqn (1.79) is a *necessary* condition if R'_1, R'_2 are to be simultaneously reducible to diagonal form. But the important point is that it is also a *sufficient* condition. To see this, suppose that R_1, R_2 are two commuting observables. Let us express them in a basis such that R_1 is diagonal. Consider an element of the commutator.

$$(R_1 R_2 - R_2 R_1)^k_j = R_{1j}^{\ l} R_{2l}^{\ k} - R_{2j}^{\ l} R_{1l}^{\ k} = (R_{1j}^{\ j} - R_{1k}^{\ k}) R_{2j}^{\ k}. \tag{1.80}$$

Since the commutator, by hypothesis, is identically zero, there are two possibilities to be considered. Either

$$R_{2j}^{\ k} = 0 \tag{1.81}$$

or

$$R_{1j}^{\ j} = R_{1k}^{\ k}. \tag{1.82}$$

If $j = k$, then eqn (1.82) is automatically satisfied and if $j \neq k$ then eqn (1.81) is satisfied unless ψ_j, ψ_k are degenerate in R_1. Thus, for the non degenerate case the result is proved. For the degenerate case, a basis for which R_1 is diagonal will not *necessarily* have R_2 diagonal. This is because R_1 on its own is not sufficient to define the basis states and another operator must be used to resolve the degeneracy. However, we can choose this operator to be R_2, and R_2 will therefore be diagonal. Thus, where the degeneracy of R_1 allows several possible choices of basis states, it is precisely this freedom of choice which allows us to make R_2 diagonal. We conclude, therefore, that it is possible to choose a set of basis states which are simultaneously eigenstates of R_1, R_2 if and only if R_1, R_2 commute. At this stage, it may seem unnecessary to insist on this rather formal property. However, it will become clear later that such commutation relations form an essential part of every aspect of our discussion of symmetry and conservation laws.

At the beginning of this section, we listed the three classes of numbers which comprise the physical content of quantum mechanics. So far we have formulated the matrix algebra of only one, namely the class of eigenvalues of all relevant observables. The remaining two follow easily. For any state, ϕ, represented by a vector, V, the expectation value of any observable, R, follows from eqn (1.8).

$$\langle r \rangle = \langle \phi | R | \phi \rangle = V^\dagger R V. \tag{1.83}$$

It is easy to see that this result is independent of the basis used:

$$V'^\dagger R' V' = V^\dagger C^\dagger C R C^{-1} C V = V^\dagger R V, \tag{1.84}$$

where we have used eqns (1.61), (1.62), (1.65), (1.72). The probability that a measurement of R will yield the eigenvalue, r_j, is

$$P = |\delta_j^i V_i|^2 = |V_j|^2. \tag{1.85}$$

Finally, and more generally, the transition probability between any two states, ϕ, χ, expressed by vectors V, U respectively is

$$P = |U^\dagger V|^2. \tag{1.86}$$

The last two equations follow directly from eqn (1.9) and are clearly independent of the basis used.

This completes the reformulation in matrix terms of the quantum mechanics introduced in Section 1.1. To sum up: we have shown that, given a set of basis states, any state function, ϕ, can be expressed as a vector, V. Given an alternative set of basis states, it can be expressed as a new vector, V', with the same dimension but different elements. V, V' are related by an equation of the form (1.61) where C is a unitary matrix. Two equivalent definitions of unitarity are given by eqns (1.54), (1.67). The latter can be used to define a *unitary operator* whether or not that operator is expressed in matrix form. An operator, R, corresponding to an observable has eigenvalues given by eqn (1.69) and is hermitian. Two equivalent definitions of hermiticity are given by eqns (1.55), (1.75), where the latter can be used even if R is not expressed as a matrix. States can be eigenstates simultaneously of two operators, R_1, R_2, if and only if R_1, R_2 commute. Finally, expectation values and transition probabilities are given by eqns (1.83), (1.86) respectively.

1.4. Dynamical operators and conservation laws

This book is concerned with symmetry and conservation principles. All detailed dynamical theories lie outside its scope. However, as some of our conclusions will be expressed as *restrictions* on the form that dynamical operators can take, it is necessary to discuss what these operators are and how they fit into the theory. In particular, since all conservation laws state that certain quantities are unchanged in certain reactions, or by the passage of time, their formulation will necessarily vary according to the dynamical language which is being used. For this reason, dynamical operators and conservation laws will be introduced together in this section and certain very general connections between them will be proved. Nothing, however, will be said about the explicit form of these operators or the truth or falsity of any dynamical theory.

It is convenient to start with the Schrödinger formulation of non-relativistic quantum mechanics. This is based on the two equations

$$H|\psi\rangle = E|\psi\rangle, \tag{1.87}$$

$$H|\psi\rangle = i\hbar \frac{\partial}{\partial t}| \psi\rangle = i\hbar|\dot\psi\rangle. \tag{1.88}$$

The former equation gives the static eigenvalues, E_j, of the Hamiltonian operator, H. The latter describes the time development of the eigenfunctions. Since the Hamiltonian corresponds to an observable, it must be hermitian and it can be written as a square matrix. Its eigenfunctions form a complete orthonormal set.

Now one very common meaning for the statement that a physical quantity is conserved is that it corresponds to an operator such that neither the operator itself nor its expectation values change with time. The consequences of this are easily derived by taking the time derivative of eqn (1.8)

$$\langle \dot r\rangle = \langle \dot\phi|R|\phi\rangle + \langle \phi|\dot R|\phi\rangle + \langle \phi|R|\dot\phi\rangle$$

$$= \frac{i}{\hbar}\langle H\phi|R|\phi\rangle + \langle \phi|\dot R|\phi\rangle - \frac{i}{\hbar}\langle \phi|R|H\phi\rangle$$

$$= \frac{i}{\hbar}\langle \phi|HR - RH|\phi\rangle + \langle \phi|\dot R|\phi\rangle, \tag{1.89}$$

where the second step uses eqn (1.88) and the last step uses eqn (1.75) and the fact that H is hermitian. Eqn (1.89) holds for *all* ϕ and it follows that if, $\langle \dot r\rangle$ and $\dot R$ are both zero then

$$HR - RH = [H, R] = 0. \tag{1.90}$$

Thus, if R is to be conserved, a necessary condition is that R, H should commute. Is it also a sufficient condition? The answer is that, in the usual Schrödinger formulation of quantum mechanics, it is. In this formulation, state functions may vary with time and the results of observations may also, of course, vary with time. But the operators corresponding to observables are considered to be fixed. The last term in eqn (1.89) is therefore zero by definition and $\langle \dot{r} \rangle$ is zero if and only if eqn (1.90) is satisfied. It is, however, worth remembering that this condition is not forced on us and that there may be occasions on which it is useful to give R some explicit time dependence.

While the Schrödinger formulation has many uses, it is sometimes desirable to express our dynamical theories in terms of operators alone. One method for doing this is easily derived from the Schrödinger formulation. Instead of using a state function, ϕ, which depends on time, we could substitute

$$|\phi\rangle \equiv U|\phi_0\rangle, \tag{1.91}$$

where ϕ_0 is the state function at time $t = 0$ and U is, by definition, an *operator* which gives its subsequent time development. U, ϕ are then functions of time, but ϕ_0 is not. Using eqn (1.8), the expectation value of any observable can be written

$$\langle r \rangle = \langle \psi_0 | U^\dagger R U | \psi_0 \rangle \equiv \langle \psi_0 | R(t) | \psi_0 \rangle, \tag{1.92}$$

where

$$R(t) \equiv U^\dagger R U. \tag{1.93}$$

But, if an observable is conserved, its expectation value does not change with time:

$$\langle \psi_0 | R | \psi_0 \rangle = \langle \psi | R | \psi \rangle, \tag{1.94}$$

and since this is true for *all* ϕ_0,

$$R = U^\dagger R U. \tag{1.95}$$

In particular

$$H = U^\dagger H U. \tag{1.96}$$

Now, in this formulation, the time dependent Schrödinger equation, (1.88), becomes

$$HU = i\hbar \dot{U}. \tag{1.97}$$

Differentiating eqn (1.93) with respect to time and using eqn (1.97), we find that

$$\dot{R}(t) = \frac{i}{\hbar}[H, R(t)] + U^\dagger \dot{R} U, \tag{1.98}$$

in analogy with eqn (1.89). If R does not depend explicitly on time, then

$$\dot{R}(t) = \frac{i}{\hbar}[H, R(t)], \tag{1.99}$$

and r is conserved if and only if $R(t)$ commutes with H. Eqn (1.99) gives an alternative description of the time development of the system. State functions are not used explicitly, but the operators corresponding to observables are now functions of time. This formulation is due to Heisenberg. It should be clear that its physical content is the same as that of the Schrödinger formulation and that the choice between the two is dictated simply by convenience.

The Schrödinger and Heisenberg formulations were devised early in the history of quantum mechanics for dealing with cases in which the detailed form of the interaction Hamiltonian was known. In particle physics, one is not so fortunate. In general, one can determine the initial state function of a system, with the particles well separated and non-interacting, and one can determine the final state function of the system; but the mechanism producing the transition between the two states has yet to be worked out. For the time being, therefore, we must use a new formalism which makes maximum use of our limited knowledge. Now it could be argued that, since all our observations can be expressed as a set of transition probabilities between various initial and final states, we should frame our physics directly in terms of transition amplitudes, rather than experimentally inaccessible operators like the Hamiltonian. This view has much to recommend it and forms the starting point for S-matrix theory. S is defined as the operator which acts on the initial state to produce the transition being studied. Thus the transition amplitude between an initial state, ψ_j, and a final state, ψ_p, can be written

$$S_p^j = \langle \psi_p | S | \psi_j \rangle. \tag{1.100}$$

The transition probability is given by the square of the modulus of this amplitude (cf. the definition, eqn (1.9), of *spontaneous* transition probability). S_p^j can be thought of as an element of a square matrix and thus S, like other operators in quantum mechanics, can be expressed in matrix form. Given a suitable set of basis vectors, it will contain a complete physical description of the interaction.

However S-matrix theory aims to do more than simply list experimental results. Certain properties of S can be determined on quite general grounds. Some arise from various symmetry or conservation laws and will be discussed later in this book. Others can be deduced from the assumption that S must be an analytic function of certain variables and these are discussed in books dealing with dispersion relations. For the time being we shall content ourselves with proving two theorems. First, the S-matrix is unitary. Secondly, an observable, r, is conserved if and only if the corresponding operator, R, commutes with S.

The unitarity of the S-matrix follows from the fact that the sum of the transition probabilities from any state, ϕ, to all possible final states is unity. One must, of course, choose a complete orthonormal set of final states, but any set of basis states will do for this purpose. Let us write ϕ as a state vector, V_j. Then

$$\begin{aligned} 1 &= \sum_i |\langle \psi_i | S | \phi \rangle|^2 \\ &= (SV)^{\dagger i}(SV)_i \\ &= V^\dagger S^\dagger S V. \end{aligned} \qquad (1.101)$$

But eqn (1.101) is satisfied for *every* possible normalized V and hence

$$S^\dagger S = I, \qquad (1.102)$$

where I is given by eqn (1.45). Comparison with eqn (1.54) shows that S is unitary.

Now, in S-matrix theory, the statement that a physical quantity is conserved means that its expectation values are the same before and after the interaction. Consider an initial state, ϕ. Then the definition of S implies that the final state can be written

$$\chi \equiv S\phi. \qquad (1.103)$$

By eqn (1.8), the initial and final expectation values for any observable, R, will be

$$\langle r_i \rangle = \langle \phi | R | \phi \rangle, \qquad (1.104)$$

$$\langle r_f \rangle = \langle \chi | R | \chi \rangle = \langle \phi | S^\dagger R S | \phi \rangle. \qquad (1.105)$$

If these expectation values are equal for *all* ϕ, then

$$R = S^\dagger R S = S^{-1} R S, \qquad (1.106)$$

$$\therefore \quad [R, S] = 0 \qquad (1.107)$$

using eqn (1.102). That is R, S commute. Conversely, if R, S commute, then the expectation values for all ϕ will be left unchanged by the interaction. Eqn (1.107) is thus a necessary and sufficient condition for conservation of R.

Finally, it may happen that two observables, R_1, R_2 are *simultaneously* conserved. They will then *both* commute with S or H. But we showed in Section 1.3 that this implies that for the basis in which S or H is diagonal, except in certain degenerate cases, R_1, R_2 will both be diagonal too. It follows that they can both be made diagonal simultaneously and will therefore commute:

$$[R_1, R_2] = 0. \tag{1.108}$$

This, then is a necessary condition, but not, of course, a sufficient one for them to be simultaneously conserved. Exceptions to this rule can arise only if S, H are simultaneously degenerate in the eigenstates of R_1, R_2.

This section has included all that we shall need to know about dynamical theories. In the following sections, we shall not usually be concerned with the explicit form of the Hamiltonian operator, H, nor the operators, R, S, corresponding to observables and transitions. We have seen that the conditions that conservation laws hold can be summed up in the three commutation relations, eqns (1.90), (1.107), and (1.108). In the next section, we shall derive analogous relations for symmetry principles. Our entire concentration is thus on *general* properties of H, R and S and we shall find that these considerations often lead to powerful and interesting results long before the detailed dynamics of a problem have been worked out.

1.5. Symmetry principles

A symmetry principle assigns to every physical state a corresponding state such that the physics of the system (that is, the set of all eigenvalues, expectation values, and transition probabilities) remains unaltered. In the present section, this idea will be formulated mathematically. First, we shall show that the definition implies rather stringent conditions on the symmetry operators themselves. Then we shall consider how other operators transform under symmetry operations. Finally, we shall use these results to write down a set of necessary and sufficient conditions which must be satisfied if a symmetry principle is to be obeyed.

All quantum mechanical operators discussed so far have been linear and have left the basis states unchanged. This has made it possible to write them as matrices and to manipulate them using elementary matrix algebra. Symmetry operators, however, are defined in a much more general fashion. Many of them correspond to operations which cannot in fact be carried out physically. Time reversal and rotations in isospin space are obvious examples. It cannot therefore be assumed that, if a state function can be expressed in terms of a particular set of basis states, then a new state produced by acting on it with a symmetry operator can also be expressed in terms of the same set of basis states. This has the consequence that we must discuss symmetry operators from a much more general standpoint and must not assume that they can always be written in matrix form. Fortunately, it turns out that many of our earlier ideas will still be valuable.

Consider a symmetry operator, T. Then, by definition, we can assign to every physical state, ϕ, a corresponding state, ϕ', given by

$$\phi' = T\phi, \tag{1.109}$$

such that the physics of the system remains unaltered. This will imply certain relationships between T and R, H, and S. It also has the immediate consequence that the transition probability between any two states, ϕ and χ say, will be unaltered.

$$|\langle\chi'|\phi'\rangle|^2 = |\langle\chi|\phi\rangle|^2 \tag{1.110}$$

cf. eqn (1.9). We shall consider the consequences of this latter requirement first. It leads to the following important theorem.

1: With suitable phase conventions, any symmetry operator, T, must be unitary and linear or anti-unitary and anti-linear.

Unitary linear operators satisfy eqns (1.67), (1.2) and anti-unitary anti-linear operators have the form

$$T = UK \tag{1.111}$$

where U is a unitary linear operator and K is the complex conjugation operator defined by

$$K\alpha = \alpha^*K, \qquad KK = I, \qquad K = K^\dagger, \tag{1.112}$$

where α is any complex number. Some simple consequences of eqns (1.111), (1.112) are

$$T^\dagger T = K^\dagger U^\dagger UK = I, \tag{1.113}$$

$$\langle T\chi|T\phi\rangle = \langle\chi|\phi\rangle^*, \tag{1.114}$$

$$T(\alpha\phi+\beta\chi) = \alpha^*T\phi+\beta^*T\chi, \tag{1.115}$$

for all states ϕ, χ, and complex numbers α, β. Eqns (1.114), (1.115) give a pair of necessary and sufficient conditions for satisfying eqn

(1.111). For this reason, they are often taken to *define* the terms anti-unitary and anti-linear. Comparing eqns (1.67), (1.114) with (1.110) shows that the theorem allows us to make statements about the *phases* of transition matrix elements as well as their moduli.

The proof of theorem (*1*) follows that of Wigner (1959). Let ψ_j be a complete orthonormal set of basis states. Then, by eqn (1.110),

$$|\langle T\psi_j|T\psi_k\rangle|^2 = |\langle \psi_j|\psi_k\rangle|^2 = \delta^j_k. \tag{1.116}$$

Thus the $T\psi_j = \psi'_j$ are also orthogonal and normalized. Further than that, they are complete. For suppose that there exists a normalized state, ψ', which is orthogonal to all the ψ'_j. Then the corresponding state, ψ, in the unprimed system would be orthogonal to all the ψ_j which is contrary to hypothesis. The ψ'_j are therefore a complete orthonormal set of basis states and any state in the primed system can be expressed in terms of them. Thus if ϕ is any arbitrary state function given by eqn (1.18), ϕ' can be written

$$\phi' = \sum_j a'_j \psi'_j. \tag{1.117}$$

Now, by eqn (1.110)

$$|a'_j| = |\langle \psi'_j|\phi'\rangle| = |\langle \psi_j|\phi\rangle| = |a_j|; \tag{1.118}$$

a_j, a'_j are thus equal in magnitude and it remains to determine their relative phases. Consider the state

$$F_{jk} \equiv \psi_j + \psi_k. \tag{1.119}$$

Then

$$F'_{jk} = T\psi_j + T\psi_k = \psi'_j + \psi'_k \tag{1.120}$$

and, by eqn (1.110)

$$|\langle F'_{jk}|\phi'\rangle| = |\langle F_{jk}|\phi\rangle|, \tag{1.121}$$

$$\therefore \quad |a'_j + a'_k| = |a_j + a_k|. \tag{1.122}$$

But, by eqn (1.118), we can write

$$a_j = |a_j| \exp(i\alpha_j), \qquad a'_j = |a_j| \exp(i\alpha'_j), \tag{1.123}$$

where the α_j, α'_j are real. Now, using eqn (1.122) we find

$$\alpha'_j - \alpha'_k = \pm(\alpha_j - \alpha_k). \tag{1.124}$$

At this point, we notice that the equations describing the behaviour of T are left unchanged if T is multiplied by an *arbitrary* phase factor.

Let us therefore choose for one index, k say,

$$\alpha'_k = \pm \alpha_k. \tag{1.125}$$

Then it follows from eqn (1.124) that for all j

$$\alpha'_j = \pm \alpha_j \tag{1.126}$$

$$\therefore \quad a'_j = a_j \text{ or } a^*_j. \tag{1.127}$$

With the first solution

$$\phi' = \sum_j a_j \psi'_j \tag{1.128}$$

and, since the ψ'_j form a complete orthonormal set, for any states, ϕ, χ, with expansion coefficients a_j, b_j respectively

$$\langle T\chi | T\phi \rangle = \sum_j b^*_j a_j = \langle \chi | \phi \rangle. \tag{1.129}$$

T is unitary. Comparing eqns (1.128), (1.2) it also follows trivially that T is linear. Similarly, the second solution of eqn (1.127) implies that T is anti-unitary and anti-linear. This completes the proof of our theorem.

So far, the discussion has been rather formal. It is now time to consider in more detail what it means physically. First, it is clear that any symmetry operation will change the initial set of basis states into a new set. The members of the new set will be in one to one correspondence with members of the old set. Where the symmetry operation can be carried out physically, they can also be expressed as linear combinations of members of the old set, and the symmetry operator can be written as a matrix. The unitary operator, C, introduced in eqns (1.30), (1.61) is the most general of such operators. But we have already met some physical examples. For instance, the time development operator, U, introduced in eqn (1.91), assigns a one to one correspondence between an initial set of basis states and another set at a later time, t. Similarly, the S-matrix assigns a one to one correspondence between basis states before and after a reaction. Both are therefore symmetry operators and, since they correspond to physical operations, both can be written as unitary matrices. By contrast, time reversal is not an operation which can be carried out physically. For time reversal the new basis states describe particles moving backwards in time and these cannot be expressed as linear combinations of basis states describing particles moving forward in time. The time reversal operator cannot therefore be written as a matrix. However it does correspond to a symmetry operation and so must obey our theorem.

Secondly, any symmetry operation leaves the magnitude of the expansion coefficients of any state vector unchanged. There are, however, two ways in which it can change their phases. One is trivial. It arises because we cannot make a direct comparison of the overall phase of any system before and after a symmetry operation. There is thus one phase which can be chosen arbitrarily without making any change in the physics. This is analogous to the overall undetermined phase which arises in any formulation of quantum mechanics and which was discussed in Section 1.1. The second way is more significant. With a suitable choice of the single arbitrary phase, the phases of the expansion coefficients will either be unchanged or reversed. These two possibilities apply respectively to unitary and anti-unitary symmetry operators. It is of course necessary to decide which of the two alternatives applies in each specific case. It turns out that symmetry operators which involve time reversal are anti-unitary while all others are unitary. The proof of this statement will be given in the next section.

Throughout this chapter, we have been emphasizing that the physical content of quantum mechanics comprises eigenvalues, the relative probabilities that each eigenvalue will be observed, and transition probabilities. It follows that, if a symmetry principle is to be obeyed, all three should be left the same. We have seen that, if transition probabilities are to be left unchanged, then severe restrictions are placed on the symmetry operators, T. It is next necessary to consider how the operators, R, corresponding to observables will change under T, and what conditions must be satisfied if their eigenvalues and expectation values are to be left unchanged.

The transformation of R can be obtained by requiring that its expectation value for any state should be left unchanged by the symmetry operation

$$\langle r \rangle = \langle \phi' | R' | \phi' \rangle = \langle \phi | R | \phi \rangle \tag{1.130}$$

$$\therefore \ \langle \phi | T^{\dagger} R' T | \phi \rangle = \langle \phi | R | \phi \rangle. \tag{1.131}$$

But, since this equation is true for *all* ϕ

$$T^{\dagger} R' T = R \tag{1.132}$$

$$\therefore \ R' = T R T^{-1}. \tag{1.133}$$

In the last step, we have used eqns (1.54), (1.113). Eqn (1.133) gives the general expression for the *transformation* of an observable, R, under a symmetry operation, T. However, if the symmetry principle is obeyed eqn (1.130) has an important further consequence. Using eqns (1.67), (1.114) and remembering that $\langle r \rangle$ is real, it gives

$$\langle \phi | R' | \phi \rangle = \langle \phi | R | \phi \rangle \tag{1.134}$$

and, since this is true for all ϕ, R and R' must be *identical*.

$$\therefore \quad R = TRT^{-1} \tag{1.135}$$

$$\therefore \quad [R, T] = 0. \tag{1.136}$$

This is a necessary and sufficient condition for the invariance of the expectation values of R under the symmetry transformation, T. It adds yet another to the growing list of commutation relations in terms of which the essential physics of this chapter can be expressed.

The final condition which must be satisfied if T is to be a valid symmetry principle is that there should exist in the primed system an eigenvalue equation analogous to eqn (1.1) and having the same eigenvalues

$$R' \psi'_j = r_j \psi'_j. \tag{1.137}$$

But, using eqns (1.109), (1.133), it is easy to see that this condition is satisfied automatically. Eqn (1.137) implies

$$TRT^{-1}T\psi_j = r_j T\psi_j, \tag{1.138}$$

and this is obtained from eqn (1.1) by multiplying both sides by T.

This completes the discussion of symmetry principles in static quantum mechanics. To sum up: by definition, a symmetry principle assigns to every physical state a corresponding state such that the physics of the system remains unaltered. The symmetry operators, T, are much more general than the other operators introduced earlier in this chapter. They do not necessarily correspond to operations which can be carried out physically and they cannot necessarily be written in matrix form. However, the definition does imply that they must be linear and unitary (eqns (1.2), (1.67)) or anti-linear and anti-unitary (eqns (1.115), (1.114)) and that they must commute with all the operators, R, corresponding to observables. These ideas are developed further in the following section.

1.6. Behaviour of dynamical operators under symmetry operations

The last section discussed the basic conditions which must be satisfied by all symmetry operators. We have not yet considered the restrictions which they imply for the time development of the system. This will be the subject matter of the present section. We shall consider in turn each of the dynamical operators introduced in Section 1.4 and the restrictions which are implied by unitary and anti-unitary symmetry operators. In each case, it will turn out that anti-unitary symmetries involve time reversal while unitary symmetries do not.

First consider the time-dependent Schrödinger equation, (1.88). Since the Hamiltonian operator, H, corresponds to an observable, it follows from eqn (1.136) that it must commute with any symmetry operator, T.

$$[H, T] = 0. \tag{1.139}$$

However, the time dependent Schrödinger equation states that, in considering the dynamics of a system, H can be replaced by the time development operator $i\hbar(\partial/\partial t)$. It follows that if the time development of the primed system is to be identical with that of the unprimed system, then

$$\left[i\hbar \frac{\partial}{\partial t}, T\right] = 0. \tag{1.140}$$

Clearly, this is true if (a) T is unitary and *does not* change the sign of t or (b) T is anti-unitary and *does* change the sign of t. This gives the first proof of the statement made earlier that anti-unitary implies time reversal and vice-versa.

The two other dynamical operators, U, S, both describe the time development of a system. U is defined in very general terms. It simply describes the change that takes place in the system during time t (cf. eqn (1.91)). For the present discussion, we shall write it explicitly as $U(t)$. S is defined as the operator which produces a particular transition. It is thus a special but very important case of U. Both are symmetry operators and hence both must satisfy equations of the form (1.65). Now, starting from eqn (1.91) and including time explicitly,

$$\langle \phi(t)|\phi(t) \rangle = 1 = \langle \phi(t)| U(t)|\phi(0) \rangle. \tag{1.141}$$

Operating with T and remembering that both sides are real

$$1 = \langle T\phi(t)|TU(t)T^{-1}|T\phi(0) \rangle. \tag{1.142}$$

Now, if T does not reverse the direction of time, the interpretation of these equations is simple. U describes the time development of the initial system and TUT^{-1} describes the time development of the primed system. If T is a good symmetry principle, then the two time developments must be identical for all ϕ. It follows that

$$U = TUT^{-1} \tag{1.143}$$

$$\therefore \quad [U, T] = 0, \tag{1.144}$$

and by exactly analogous reasoning

$$[S, T] = 0. \tag{1.145}$$

However, if T involves time reversal, eqn (1.142) becomes

$$1 = \langle \phi'(-t) | TU(t)T^{-1} | \phi'(0) \rangle. \tag{1.146}$$

That is, $TU(t)T^{-1}$ describes the time development of the primed system *with time running backwards*. Thus, if T is a good symmetry principle,

$$U(-t) = TU(t)T^{-1}. \tag{1.147}$$

Now it follows from the definition of U that

$$U(-t)U(t) = 1, \tag{1.148}$$

and from eqn (1.65) that

$$U^{\dagger}(t)U(t) = 1, \tag{1.149}$$

$$\therefore \quad U = (TUT^{-1})^{\dagger}. \tag{1.150}$$

It is important to be clear about the interpretation of this equation. The left hand side is an operator which acts on an *earlier* state in the *unprimed* system to produce a *later* state. The right hand side is an operator which acts on a *later* state in the *primed* system to produce an *earlier* one. Explicitly, for an arbitrary initial state ϕ and final state χ

$$\langle \chi | U | \phi \rangle = \langle \phi' | (TUT^{-1})^{\dagger} | \chi' \rangle. \tag{1.151}$$

Simple manipulation of this equation gives

$$\langle \chi | U | \phi \rangle = \langle \chi' | TUT^{-1} | \phi' \rangle^*$$
$$= \langle T\chi | TU\phi \rangle^*. \tag{1.152}$$

And comparison with eqn (1.114) shows that T is anti-unitary. By exactly the same reasoning, the S operator must satisfy

$$S = (TST^{-1})^{\dagger} \tag{1.153}$$

with the same interpretation regarding initial and final states.

To sum up: if the time development of a system is to be invariant under a symmetry operation, T, then a necessary and sufficient condition is that T should commute with the Hamiltonian. Similarly, if T does not involve time reversal, the condition is that it must commute with the time development operators U, S. However, if T does involve time reversal, then U, S must transform according to eqns (1.150), (1.153), where in each case it is assumed that not only does the right hand side refer to the primed system, but also that the order of initial and final states is reversed. In any case, T is anti-unitary if and only if it involves time reversal.

1.7. The relationship between symmetry and conservation principles

In preceding sections, we have introduced symmetry and conservation principles and have related them to the operators and states which occur in quantum mechanics. It remains to relate them to each other. In this section we prove a very important theorem:

2: From every conservation law, it is possible to construct a unitary symmetry principle.

Consider an operator, R, which corresponds to a conserved observable. Then we have seen that it must commute with the Hamiltonian, H, and the S-matrix. We have also seen that it must be hermitian. Now consider the operator

$$T = e^{iR} \tag{1.154}$$

$$\equiv I + iR + \frac{(iR)^2}{2!} + \frac{(iR)^3}{3!} + \dots . \tag{1.155}$$

Now, by construction, T is linear and it also satisfies

$$TT^\dagger = \exp(iR)\exp(-iR^\dagger) = \exp[i(R - R^\dagger)] = I, \tag{1.156}$$

since R is hermitian. Hence T is unitary. Moreover it can operate on any state to produce a new state. Thus T can be a symmetry operator. But the important point is that, if R commutes with H, S then *so does* T and we have seen that each of these commutation rules gives a necessary and sufficient condition that the symmetry principle should be obeyed. Thus, if R is the observable in a conservation law, then T is the operator in a symmetry principle and the theorem is proved. The theorem is, in fact, completely general and can also be proved within the framework of classical mechanics.

Note that, while eqn (1.154) gives one way of constructing a symmetry principle, it is by no means unique. Any relation of the form

$$T = \exp[if(R)] \qquad (1.157)$$

where $f(R)$ is a function of R with real coefficients would do. Even eqn (1.157) by no means exhausts the possibilities. It may happen, for instance, that R is both hermitian *and* unitary and thus that a single operator will provide both a symmetry and a conservation principle. We shall meet with two examples of this in the next chapter. Finally note that what we have proved is that every conservation law implies a symmetry principle. Most symmetry principles in turn have corresponding conservation laws, but there are some exceptions. Time reversal, for instance, is anti-linear and so cannot be expressed as a function of a linear observable. There is therefore no corresponding conservation law. Nevertheless, the relationship is usually a reciprocal one and in the following chapters we shall usually be concerned with both aspects of the principles.

The rest of the book will be devoted to a discussion of the various symmetry and conservation principles which occur in particle physics. We shall see that most of them are obeyed in only a restricted range of interactions and it will be necessary to explore the range of each in detail. Fortunately, there is considerable regularity, and it is usually possible to say of a principle that it is obeyed in *all* strong or *all* electromagnetic or *all* weak interactions. Many of the important results are applicable to strong interactions only and our treatment will be heavily biassed towards these. However, one should avoid the idea that the strong interaction has a greater *intrinsic* symmetry than the weak. The weak interaction proceeds very much more slowly than the strong and hence is most often observed when it violates some selection rule which is satisfied by the latter. A little reflection will convince the reader that the converse situation would be extremely difficult to observe. Similarly, one should avoid the idea that symmetry principles must be exactly obeyed if they are to be interesting and useful. On the contrary, many of the most important sections of this book will be concerned with broken symmetries and it will be seen that it is precisely *because* they are broken that they lead to interesting and important results.

Problems

Suppose that for a quantum mechanical system the Hamiltonian, H, and an observable, R, are given by

$$H = \begin{pmatrix} 7 & 7\sqrt{3} & -6(\sqrt{3})i \\ 7\sqrt{3} & 21 & -18i \\ 6(\sqrt{3})i & 18i & 52 \end{pmatrix} E_0, \qquad R = \begin{pmatrix} 11 & -5\sqrt{3} & 2(\sqrt{3})i \\ -5\sqrt{3} & 1 & 6i \\ -2(\sqrt{3})i & -6i & -12 \end{pmatrix} \frac{\hbar}{16}.$$

(a) Show that R is conserved.

(b) Find its eigenvalues.

(c) Find the energies of the states corresponding to each of these eigenvalues.

(d) Give as much information as you can about the following states

$$\phi = \begin{pmatrix} \frac{3}{4}\sqrt{\frac{3}{2}} \\ \frac{1}{4\sqrt{2}}\sqrt{\frac{1}{2}} \\ \frac{-i}{2}\sqrt{\frac{1}{2}} \end{pmatrix}, \qquad \chi = \begin{pmatrix} (\sqrt{3}+1)/4\sqrt{2} \\ (\sqrt{3}+3)/4\sqrt{2} \\ i(\sqrt{3}-1)/2\sqrt{2} \end{pmatrix}.$$

(e) What is the transition probability between them?

(f) Find a symmetry operator corresponding to R, express it in matrix form, and verify that the matrix is unitary.

2

THE DISCRETE SYMMETRIES P, C, AND T

THE subject matter of this chapter is rather different from that of the rest of the book. Each discrete symmetry principle corresponds to a definite inversion and can be described in terms of a single operator. Applied twice, the operator leaves the system unchanged. All other symmetry operations which are of interest in particle physics involve an infinite range of transformations. This limitation leads to certain selection rules which merit discussion on their own. The derivation of these rules is described in Section 2.1. It must be emphasized, however, that the principles to be discussed are primarily *symmetry* principles. It is true that the selection rules for parity and charge conjugation are often expressed as conservation laws, but it is shown that the quantities conserved are observable only in a very limited sense and have by no means all the usual properties discussed in the last chapter. Nor does the usual relationship (eqn (1.157)) between symmetry and conservation laws hold in this case. Sections 2.2–5 are devoted to a discussion of the individual symmetries and the limits to their validity. The discussion proceeds from first principles and relies heavily on the results derived in the last chapter. Examples are introduced for illustration, and the types of prediction are considered systematically, but no attempt is made to provide a comprehensive list of the applications of the principles. For further information and references, the reader is referred to the literature (e.g. Sakurai 1964, Nilsson 1967).

2.1. Discrete symmetries and selection rules

This section is concerned with the general properties of discrete symmetries and of the selection rules which can be deduced from them. Let us start with a definition. A discrete symmetry operator is a symmetry operator which, if applied twice to any physical system, will leave that system unchanged. Thus space inversion (parity), time reversal, and rotation by π radians about some axis in space are all examples of discrete symmetry operations. The statement that the system should be unchanged looks very like the statement made in Section 1.5 when defining all symmetry principles. The difference is that, while all symmetry principles demand the same behaviour from an initial state and its corresponding transformed state, the demand that the system be unchanged means that the transformed state *is* the initial state. Every statement about observable properties which is true of one is also true of the other. The only quantity left undetermined is the usual arbitrary phase since, of course, the initial and transformed states cannot interfere with each other. Thus, if T is a discrete symmetry operator,

$$TT = \alpha I \tag{2.1}$$

where I is the identity operator and α is a complex number of unit magnitude.

Now, it is easy to see not only that the double operator, TT, is an exact symmetry for all interactions but also that it is linear and unitary regardless of whether T itself is unitary or anti-unitary. Hence, by eqn (1.145), it must commute with the S-matrix. It follows that, for any two states, ϕ, χ, and an arbitrarily chosen transition operator, S,

$$\langle \chi|S|\phi \rangle = \langle TT\chi|S|TT\phi \rangle$$

$$= \alpha^*_\chi \alpha_\phi \langle \chi|S|\phi \rangle, \tag{2.2}$$

where α_ϕ, α_χ are the values of α for ϕ, χ respectively. There are two possibilities. Either the S-matrix element between ϕ, χ is zero, or $\alpha^*_\chi \alpha_\phi = 1$. Thus, if a transition between ϕ, χ is possible by *any physical process whatsoever* then

$$\alpha_\phi = \alpha_\chi. \tag{2.3}$$

Conversely, if eqn (2.3) is not obeyed then no transition is possible.

The application of this result to time reversal leads to an important selection rule. Consider eqns (1.65), (1.113). They state that any symmetry operator, T, must satisfy

$$TT^\dagger = I \tag{2.4}$$

$$\therefore \quad TT = \alpha TT^\dagger. \tag{2.5}$$

Multiplying on the left by T^{-1} and on the right by T,

$$TT = T^{-1}\alpha TT^\dagger T,$$

$$\therefore \quad \alpha I = T^{-1}\alpha T. \tag{2.6}$$

This gives no useful information if T is unitary, but if T is *anti-unitary*

$$\alpha = \alpha^*$$

$$\therefore \quad \alpha = \pm 1. \tag{2.7}$$

Now it was shown in Section 1.6 that the time reversal operator is anti-unitary. It follows that in this case

$$TT = \pm I. \tag{2.8}$$

No physical transitions whatsoever are possible between states for which the eigenvalue of TT is $+1$ and those for which it is -1. But we shall show in Section 4.7 that bosons lie in the former group of states and fermions in the latter. Bosons cannot, therefore, change into fermions and vice versa. This is the law of *conservation of statistics*. Selection rules of this kind, which apply without restriction to all types of interaction are known as *superselection rules*. They will be discussed in more detail in the next chapter.

Now consider the selection rules which can be derived for the unitary discrete symmetries. Eqn (2.1) implies that, in a sense, *all* physical states are eigenstates of TT. However, for unitary symmetries the eigenvalue, α, is completely undetermined and there is no useful physical information to be obtained. The operator TT is not necessarily hermitian and does not correspond to an observable. However, there will be certain physical states for which the statements which we have made about the double operator TT can also be made about T itself, where T is now a discrete *unitary* symmetry. These are the states which are invariant under T except for a possible phase change

$$T\phi = \beta\phi \tag{2.9}$$

where β is a complex number of unit magnitude. At first sight, it appears that β, like α, is unobservable and so contains no useful physical information. But in fact the situation is not quite so bad as this. Consider two states, ϕ, χ, which are both eigenstates of T in the sense that they satisfy eqn (2.9). Suppose further that there exists some operator, S say, which produces transitions between them. Then a comparison of eqns (2.1), (2.3), (2.9) shows that $\beta_\phi{}^2 = \beta_\chi{}^2$ and hence that

$$\beta_\phi = \pm\beta_\chi. \tag{2.10}$$

Now let S' be any transition operator for which T is an exact symmetry. By eqn (1.145), T will commute with S' and since it is, by hypothesis, unitary

$$\langle \chi | S' | \phi \rangle = \langle T\chi | S' | T\phi \rangle$$

$$= \beta^*_{\chi} \beta_{\phi} \langle \chi | S' | \phi \rangle. \qquad (2.11)$$

Once again, there are two possibilities. Either the S'-matrix element between ϕ, χ is zero or $\beta^*_{\chi} \beta_{\phi} = 1$. Comparison with eqn (2.10) shows that, if $\beta_{\phi} = -\beta_{\chi}$, then S' can produce no transition between ϕ, χ, but, if $\beta_{\phi} = \beta_{\chi}$ then S' *may perhaps* produce a transition between them. Thus, by observing which transitions occur, it is often possible to state whether the values of β for two given states are the same or opposite. So, while *absolute* values of β cannot be determined, *relative* values often can and, indeed, there are only two possibilities. If T were the parity operator, for instance, these two possibilities would correspond to the same and opposite parities. This is the essence of the selection rules which follow from the invariance of certain transition operators under parity, charge conjugation, and so on. They allow us to divide states into two classes and to say that transitions between the two classes will be forbidden for certain interactions. Several features of the discussion, however, need further elucidation.

First, the whole scheme for comparing the values of β for two states, ϕ, χ, depends on the assumption that there exists at least one transition, S, which allows ϕ to change into χ (eqn (2.2)). One then considers another transition, S', which is chosen such that it commutes with T, and observes whether or not *this* transition allows ϕ to change into χ. But suppose that there is *no possible S* which satisfies the first condition. No charged state, for instance, can ever change to a wholly uncharged state. In this case, it is experimentally impossible to determine the relative values of β_{ϕ}, β_{χ} and they must be fixed *by definition*. We return to this point in the next chapter.

Secondly, we have used the term *state* in a quite general sense. It is sometimes possible to express a given state, ψ say, as the product of two other states, ϕ, χ

$$\psi = \phi\chi. \qquad (2.12)$$

This would occur, for instance, if ψ were a final state with two well separated reaction products. In this case, TT acts on both ϕ and χ

$$TT\psi = \alpha_{\phi}\alpha_{\chi}\phi\chi,$$

$$\therefore \quad \alpha\psi = \alpha_{\phi}\alpha_{\chi}. \qquad (2.13)$$

This leads to a curious exception to the conclusion that we can determine relative but not absolute values of α. For suppose that a given state can decay into either two or three particles and that these particles are identical. K^0, for instance, can decay into either two or three π^0. Then it follows that

$$\alpha_{\pi^0}{}^2 = \alpha_{\pi^0}{}^3$$

$$\therefore \quad \alpha_{\pi^0} = 1. \tag{2.14}$$

Thus α_{π^0} can immediately be assigned a unique value. Such instances are rare, however, and in general the physics is invariant under changes in α. For this reason, it is usual to set α to unity *by definition* and thus to require that for all unitary discrete symmetries

$$TT = I. \tag{2.15}$$

Eqn (2.9) then becomes

$$T\phi = \pm \phi. \tag{2.16}$$

If T is the parity operator, for instance, the alternatives would correspond to positive and negative parity.

Thirdly, the assertion that two states have the same value of β can be made with more confidence than the assertion that they have opposite values. The former is based on the observation that a particular transition occurs; the latter simply means that a transition has been looked for but not found. Now, many factors may inhibit a transition. There may be more than one selection rule at work or there may be some dynamical inhibition. It is therefore necessary to be very cautious when drawing inferences from evidence of this sort. Once again, however, there are exceptions. Suppose that a state, ψ, can be expressed by eqn (2.12) and that β_ϕ is known to be -1, then the occurrence of the transition $\psi \to \psi'$ through a matrix element of S' would imply

$$\beta_\chi = -\beta_{\psi'}. \tag{2.17}$$

An example of this will be discussed in the next section.

Finally, notice that eqn (2.16) has the form of an eigenvalue equation. With the appropriate phase convention, T is hermitian and, in a very limited sense, its eigenvalues, β, are *observable*. Furthermore, the discussion of eqn (2.11) tells us that β is conserved in the transition S'. Thus the symmetry principle, T, has led to a selection rule which can be expressed as a *conservation law*. If T is the parity operator and the two possibilities in eqn (2.16) are interpreted as positive and negative parity, then parity is said to be *conserved* in the transition S'.

The language is very useful, but it is important to realize that the new laws are conservation laws only in a very limited sense and that by no means all the statements made in Chapter 1 apply to them. We have already considered some of these limitations. Except in some very special circumstances, one measures relative but not absolute eigenvalues and even this is not always possible. Moreover, even after making the definition (2.15) the eigenvalues do not have the usual properties. They can take only two values, ± 1; and the eigenvalue of a compound state will be the *product* rather than the *sum* of the eigenvalues of the constituents (cf. eqn 1.2a). However, there is a more fundamental difference than this. The operators, R, corresponding to observables describe a physical operation which is actually carried out when a measurement is made. If ϕ is expressed in terms of a particular set of basis states, then $R\phi$ can be expressed in terms of the same set. R can be written as a square matrix and all physical states can be expressed as linear combinations of eigenstates of R. These facts were used to derive many of the results given in Chapter 1. But, for discrete symmetries, the whole measurement process is entirely different. The operators, T, are *symmetry* operators and do not in general describe operations which can actually be carried out physically. If ϕ is expressed in terms of a particular set of basis states, it by no means follows that $T\phi$ can be expressed in terms of the same set (cf. discussion in Section 1.5). Thus T cannot be written as a square matrix. Nor can we apply it to any arbitrary state and automatically obtain an eigenvalue. Thus physical states cannot always be expressed as linear combinations of eigenstates of T and expectation value has no meaning. Nor will T necessarily commute with conserved observables unless we add the rider that ϕ, $T\phi$ must each be expanded in terms of the appropriate set of basis states. Finally, the relationship, eqn (1.157), between a conservation law and the corresponding symmetry principle has no meaning. These remarks will be illustrated by examples in the following section. For our present purpose, it is sufficient to point out that these very severe limitations exist. Failure to realize this is a frequent source of confused thinking.

So far, we have assumed that we know whether each transition operator, S', commutes with each discrete symmetry, T. The selection rules can then be used to assign values of β to certain physical states. However, it may happen that the validity of a particular symmetry principle is called into question. It is then possible to apply two classes of test. In the first, T is treated as a *symmetry* principle and we test the invariance of an interaction under T. That is, we either look for behaviour which would not be invariant under the transformation, or compare directly the behaviour of a state with that of its transformed state. In the second, T is treated as a conservation law or selection rule. We then test to see whether, within our framework of definitions, values of β can be assigned to states in a consistent manner. If two experiments give opposite values to β for the same state, then the selection rule has broken down. For instance, if a definite physical state can decay into each of two different eigenstates of T and these have opposite values of the eigenvalue, β, then each decay would determine the eigenvalue of the initial state, but the two would give opposite results, thus proving the selection rule invalid. (It is, of course, an essential part of the argument that the initial state should be a definite physical state and not a degenerate mixture of two states with opposite values of β. In the latter case, the experiment would prove nothing.) Examples from both classes of test will be discussed in the following sections.

Before leaving the subject, notice that there is one major practical difficulty. A result deduced from a given symmetry principle may well follow also from another quite separate principle. Hence if the result is *untrue* then *both* principles are violated, but if it is *true* then this is not necessarily evidence for *either*. In what follows, a symmetry principle is said to be correct if it makes predictions which have been tested and found to be true and which do not seem to follow from any other principle. It is never possible to make stronger positive statements than this.

2.2. Parity

The parity operation is defined as that operation which inverts all three spatial coordinates

$$x \rightarrow -x, \qquad y \rightarrow -y, \qquad z \rightarrow -z. \tag{2.18}$$

Using this definition, it is possible to assign to every physical state a transformed state. Parity is therefore a unitary symmetry. Clearly also, if applied twice to any physical system, it will leave that system unchanged. It is therefore discrete.

The action of the parity operator on various observables is easily derived. It follows from eqn (2.18) that position, $\mathbf{r}$, and momentum, $\mathbf{p}$, transform according to

$$T\mathbf{r}T^{-1} = -\mathbf{r}, \qquad T\mathbf{p}T^{-1} = -\mathbf{p}, \tag{2.19}$$

where T is the parity operator. (Note that T is used throughout this chapter when representing any discrete symmetry operator.) Angular momentum, $\mathbf{L}$, has the form $\mathbf{r} \times \mathbf{p}$ and so must satisfy

$$T\mathbf{L}T^{-1} = \mathbf{L}. \tag{2.20}$$

We shall also see in Chapter 4 that intrinsic spin, $\boldsymbol{\sigma}$, satisfies the same transformation law. However, helicity, which is the cosine, $\hat{\boldsymbol{\sigma}} \cdot \hat{\mathbf{p}}$, of the angle between the spin and momentum vectors satisfies

$$T\hat{\boldsymbol{\sigma}} \cdot \hat{\mathbf{p}}T^{-1} = -\hat{\boldsymbol{\sigma}} \cdot \hat{\mathbf{p}} \tag{2.21}$$

where the $\hat{}$ symbol is used to indicate a unit vector. Most other observables are scalar quantities and so are left unchanged.

In what follows, parity will first be treated as a symmetry principle and then as a selection rule. In each case, its physical consequences will be derived and we shall finally consider the class of interactions for which these consequences hold. As a symmetry principle, it asserts that to every physical state there can be assigned a parity conjugate state such that the physics of the system remains unaltered. This has consequences for both interacting and non-interacting states.

First, consider an arbitrary non interacting state. We require that it should be possible to find a corresponding parity-conjugate state which will have identical properties *provided that they are measured in a parity-conjugate frame of reference*. It is therefore necessary to consider how various observables behave under the parity operation. Scalar properties, such as charge or axial vector properties, such as angular momentum, are left unchanged by parity and so present no problem. The parity conjugate of a positively charged particle, for instance will be another positively charged particle. Now eqns (2.19), (2.21) state that certain kinematic observables change sign under parity, but these again present no problem provided that they can be varied at will. For instance, if a proton has position, $\mathbf{r}$, and momentum, $\mathbf{p}$, then its parity conjugate would be another proton with position, $-\mathbf{r}$, and momentum, $-\mathbf{p}$. This parity conjugate clearly represents a perfectly possible state. In fact, useful predictions arise only for certain pseudoscalar quantities which, by definition, change sign under parity but which cannot always be varied at will. Consider helicity, for example. By eqn (2.21), helicity changes sign under parity. Hence, if a particle is observed with a particular helicity, it should be possible to observe a parity-conjugate particle with opposite helicity. But the neutrino is known to have fixed negative helicity (Goldhaber *et al.* 1958).

The parity conjugate of a given neutrino would be another neutrino *with positive helicity*. But no such neutrino has ever been found. This immediately gives evidence that parity is not an exact symmetry of nature.

Secondly, consider the predictions which can be made about interactions. They were given formally in eqns (1.139), (1.144), (1.145):

$$[H, T] = [U, T] = [S, T] = 0.$$

These equations state essentially that the operators describing the time development of any system must have the same form in two parity-conjugate frames of reference. In practice, this statement can be interpreted in two ways. We can think of it as referring to a *single* physical system and stating that the descriptions of that system *in two parity-conjugate frames of reference* satisfy the same physical laws. This is called the *passive formulation*. Alternatively, we can think of it as relating the properties of *two different* physical systems, set up so that one is the parity conjugate of the other, when both systems are viewed *in the same frame of reference*. This is called the *active formulation*. In either case, the relations are simple and geometrical and the experimental predictions are conceptually straightforward.

A simple example of an interaction in which parity is not an exact symmetry occured in the famous experiment of Wu *et al.* (1957). These and other workers showed essentially that the angular distribution of electrons from the β decay of ^{60}Co nuclei has the form

$$P = a + b\boldsymbol{\sigma} \cdot \mathbf{p} \tag{2.22}$$

where $\boldsymbol{\sigma}$ is the spin of the ^{60}Co nucleus, $\mathbf{p}$ is the momentum of the outgoing electron and a and b are constants. The first term is invariant under the parity operation, while the second changes sign (cf. eqn (2.21)). Thus the description of the decay is clearly different in the two conjugate frames of reference and so the dynamical laws must also be different. This immediately establishes that parity is not an exact symmetry for this decay.

Perhaps even more striking is the experiment of Culligan *et al.* (1959) who examined the decays

$$\mu^{\pm} \to e^{\pm} + \nu + \bar{\nu},$$

and showed that the positrons had positive helicity and the electrons negative helicity. Since helicity changes sign under parity, each of these results on its own shows that parity is not an exact symmetry of nature.

These two experiments can also be analysed in a slightly different way. An important special consequence of eqn (1.145) is that the expectation value of any pseudoscalar quantity which can be observed in the final state of a decay must be zero. Consider a transition between an initial state, ϕ, and a final state, $\chi \equiv S\phi$. Now let R be an operator corresponding to an observable. Its expectation value in the final state will be

$$\langle \chi|R|\chi \rangle = \langle S\phi|R|S\phi \rangle$$
$$= \langle TS\phi|TRT^{-1}|TS\phi \rangle$$
$$= \langle ST\phi|TRT^{-1}|ST\phi \rangle, \tag{2.23}$$

where T is the parity operator and we have used eqn (1.67) and the fact that S, T commute. Consider the meaning of this equation. TRT^{-1} is the operator, R', obtained by operating on R with T (cf. eqn (1.133)). ϕ is the initial state and can be defined by its expectation values for a suitable set of observables. If it is a stationary state and parity is an exact symmetry, then eqn (1.136) will hold for all observables and $T\phi$ will have exactly the same properties. $T\phi$ can therefore differ from ϕ at most by an unobservable phase factor and can be replaced by ϕ in any equation in which it occurs. Therefore

$$\langle \chi|R|\chi \rangle = \langle S\phi|R'|S\phi \rangle$$
$$= \langle \chi|R'|\chi \rangle. \tag{2.24}$$

But, if R is a pseudoscalar, then R, R' have *opposite* expectation values. Both sides of eqn (2.24) must therefore be zero and the result is proved. Applying this result to the decay of ^{60}Co (eqn (2.22)), it is clear that the expectation value for the pseudoscalar quantity, $\boldsymbol{\sigma} \cdot \mathbf{p}$, is non-zero. This immediately shows that parity is not an exact symmetry. Equally, in the experiment of Culligan *et al.*, a non zero expectation value was found for the pseudoscalar quantity, helicity, and the same conclusion can be drawn.

It so happens that all three cases of parity violation discussed so far involve neutrinos. In the first, it was argued that the fact that the neutrino has a definite helicity is itself evidence that parity can not be an exact symmetry of nature. The other two examples were of decays in which neutrinos were produced. It might be supposed that all three violations are ultimately due to the same phenomenon—the existence of the intrinsically parity-asymmetric neutrino. It is therefore worth stressing that there are many interactions for which parity is not an exact symmetry but which do not involve neutrinos. Consider, for instance, the production and decay of Λ^0

$$\pi^- + p \rightarrow \Lambda^0 + K^0,$$

$$\Lambda^0 \rightarrow \pi^- + p. \tag{2.25}$$

The first is a strong interaction which can proceed through a resonant state. The second is a weak interaction. Let $\mathbf{p}_\Lambda$, $\mathbf{p}_K$, $\mathbf{p}_\pi$ be the momenta respectively of the Λ^0, K^0, and decay π^-. It is found experimentally that the expectation value

$$\langle \mathbf{p}_\pi \cdot (\mathbf{p}_\Lambda \times \mathbf{p}_K) \rangle > 0. \tag{2.26}$$

(See references given by Sakurai 1964.) That is, more of the decay pions come up from the interaction plane than go down into it. But the momentum triple product is a pseudoscalar and hence parity is not an exact symmetry in at least one of the two interactions (2.25). Further investigation shows that the parity violation is confined to the second interaction.

It is worth remarking that the reader may have been tempted to think that the detailed discussion of eqns (2.23), (2.24) was quite unnecessary. He might regard it as intuitively obvious that a non-zero expectation value for a pseudoscalar observable *must* imply parity violation. In this case, of course, his intuition would be correct. But this sort of reasoning should be used very cautiously. Consider time reversal, for instance. Momentum is one of the quantities which changes sign under time reversal and it follows that the momentum triple product in eqn (2.26) must also change sign. Nevertheless, eqn (2.26) does *not* imply time reversal non-invariance. The reason for this depends on the difference between unitary and anti-unitary symmetry operators and is by no means obvious. It is discussed in Section 2.4.

Next, let us treat parity as a conservation law or selection rule. The basic ideas were discussed in Section 2.1. Relative parities between two states can be determined if three conditions are met. First, there must be some physical process (not necessarily parity-conserving) which causes transitions between the two. Secondly, the states must be invariant under the parity operation except for a possible phase factor. Thirdly, there must be some *parity-conserving* process which will allow transitions between the two *provided that they have the same parity.* The statement that they have the same parity is now equivalent to the statement that the latter transitions occur. We remarked that if the latter transitions do not occur then the conclusion is less clear. It could be that the parities of the two states are opposite, but it could be that some other selection rule is operating. Fortunately, there is usually a way out of this dilemma. If a state has two components which have relative orbital angular momentum, l, then this orbital angular momentum contributes a factor $(-1)^l$ to the parity of the combined system. Thus, by determining the orbital angular momentum states in which transitions occur, it can be possible to make statements about relative parities with confidence, even when these parities are opposite. When we have discovered a group of states which is known to have the opposite parity from another group of states, then the relative parity of any new state can be determined by comparison with the members of each group in turn.

It is sometimes even possible to determine absolute parities. Suppose that the transition

$$\psi \rightarrow \phi\chi \tag{2.27}$$

occurs by a parity-conserving process and that the relative parities of ϕ, χ are known. This transition then allows us to determine the absolute parity of ψ. The only convention used is that eqn (2.15) should hold. An example of this reasoning is given below.

This discussion of parity as a selection rule has taken us a long way from the simple geometrical idea of parity as a symmetry principle. If no particles are created or destroyed in an interaction, of course, the selection rule governs transitions between various configurations and so is primarily geometrical in content. But, if particles *are* created or destroyed, then it is necessary to find an *intrinsic* parity for each particle in order to give meaning to the rule. Since it is often possible to determine only relative parities, a certain number of intrinsic parities must be assigned *by definition*. The number of definitions which must be made and the extent to which the whole scheme is arbitrary will be discussed in the next chapter.

Many of these ideas can be illustrated by a simple example. Consider the capture of a π^- by a deuteron when both particles are at rest. One capture mode which has been observed is

$$\pi^- + d \rightarrow n + n. \tag{2.28}$$

Now suppose that the spins of π^-, d, n are known to be $0, 1, \frac{1}{2}$ respectively.

Then, since the capture is made at rest, the total angular momentum of the initial state is 1 and, by conservation of angular momentum, the same value must hold for the final state. Expressed spectroscopically, the latter has four possible configurations—$^3S_1$, $^1P_1$, $^3P_1$, $^3D_1$. However the neutrons are identical fermions and so, by the Pauli principle, must have a totally antisymmetrical space-spin state function. Triplet states have a symmetrical spin function and so must have odd orbital angular momentum; singlet states have an antisymmetrical spin function and so must have even angular momentum. Thus the only permitted state is $^3P_1$. Now consider parity. The final state consists of two neutrons and so, *regardless* of whether an individual neutron has odd or even intrinsic parity, the two together must have *even* intrinsic parity. But, since they are in a P state, the factor $(-1)^l$ means that the total parity must be odd. By conservation of parity, the total parity of the initial state must also be odd. This is an example of a reaction of the form (2.27) which allows us to make an *absolute* assignment of parity to a particular state. No intrinsic parities need be defined and no conventions other than that in eqn (2.15) need be introduced. It is also a case in which a knowledge of angular momentum has made it possible to show that two states, in this case π^-, d, have *opposite* intrinsic parities. However, in order to assign a definite parity to π^-, it is necessary to introduce some definitions. With the usual convention, the intrinsic parities of both proton and neutron are taken to be even by definition. (See Chapter 3.) It can be shown that this entails that the intrinsic parity of the deuteron should also be even and hence that the intrinsic parity of π^- is odd. This reasoning is characteristic of the arguments used to assign intrinsic parities and frequent examples will be found in the literature.

We remarked in the last section that the unitary discrete symmetries could be considered as observables in only a very limited sense. The argument was a rather formal one and took as its starting point the fact that discrete symmetries, unlike measurements of observables, are not operations which can actually be carried out physically. It was then shown that most of the properties of observables derived in Chapter 1 could not hold for discrete symmetries. The specific example of parity may help to make the point clear. In the last section, we showed how parity could be determined for a given state, ϕ say, *provided that* it satisfied eqn (2.9) where $\beta = \pm 1$. Consider the restrictions which must apply to such parity eigenstates. The expectation value of momentum, $\mathbf{p}$, is given by

$$\langle \mathbf{p} \rangle = \langle \phi | \mathbf{p} | \phi \rangle = \langle T\phi | T\mathbf{p}\phi \rangle$$

$$= - \langle T\phi | \mathbf{p}T\phi \rangle = -\beta^2 \langle \phi | \mathbf{p} | \phi \rangle$$

$$= - \langle \mathbf{p} \rangle; \qquad\qquad (2.29)$$

where we have used the facts that T is unitary (eqn (1.67)) and that $\mathbf{p}$, T anticommute (eqn (2.19)). Thus eigenstates of parity must have zero expectation value for momentum. By analogous reasoning, they must be symmetrical about the origin and must have zero expectation value for helicity. It follows that the vast majority of physical states are not parity eigenstates and so can have no value of β. (The most important exceptions are the static eigenstates of any parity-conserving Hamiltonian, H. Remember that, by eqn (1.139), H, T commute.) It may be objected that perhaps physical states can be expressed as *linear combinations* of parity eigenstates and that the parity *expectation value* could be measured by determining their transition probabilities to various parity eigenstates. An obvious reply is that, since momentum is a conserved quantity, the final states of an interaction will no more be parity eigenstates than the initial states. Thus, it is simply not possible to make a set of measurements on an arbitrary state and so determine its parity expectation value. Further than that, some states can *not* be expressed as linear combinations of parity eigenstates. For instance, all neutrinos have negative helicity. But, since parity eigenstates have zero expectation value for helicity, no neutrino state can ever be a parity eigenstate or a linear combination of parity eigenstates. For the same reason, parity can not be expressed as a square matrix. A square matrix acting on a physical state will always produce a linear combination of basis states which is, in fact, another physical state. But parity, acting on a neutrino, produces a non-physical state—a neutrino with positive helicity—and so no matrix representation is possible. We therefore emphasize that, while 'parity conservation' provides a useful selection rule, it has no further consequences than that.

This completes the discussion of the physical consequences which can be derived if parity is an exact symmetry. We next consider the class of interactions for which these consequences hold. There is abundant evidence that they hold for all strong and electromagnetic interactions (see, for example, Nilsson 1967). This means not only that these interactions have the required spatial symmetry, but also that they allow us to make a consistent assignment of intrinsic parities such that the selection rule is always satisfied. However, it has been clear for many years that parity is not an exact symmetry when weak interactions are involved and that the violation may be very large. The first evidence for this was the famous 'τ–θ puzzle' in which what is now known as the K-meson or kaon was observed to decay into either two or three pions. Since, as we have seen, the pion has odd parity and since the components of the final state have no relative orbital angular momentum, the two and three pion states must have opposite parity. It therefore appeared that the kaon could not be assigned an intrinsic parity in a consistent way and that the selection rule had broken down. However, this evidence on its own was not quite conclusive. It was still possible that two different particles had been found—the θ, which decayed into two pions, and the τ, which decayed into three. But the famous ^{60}Co experiment of Wu et al. (1957) permitted only one interpretation. Parity, considered as a symmetry principle, could not be universally valid. Since 1957, parity violation has become commonplace, but it has been observed only when the weak interaction is involved.

Note that this last statement is not quite the same as the statement that parity is violated by the weak interaction *on its own*. Consider the 'τ–θ puzzle'. This is evidence for parity violation provided that the intrinsic parity of the pion is known to be negative. But the intrinsic parity of the pion is deduced from its behaviour *in the strong and electromagnetic interactions*. Thus the puzzle shows that it is not possible to define parity in a *consistent* fashion for strong, electromagnetic, and weak interactions. It does not show that a valid selection rule is impossible for the weak interaction alone. Similarly, the experiment of Culligan et al. shows that parity is violated in muon decay, *provided that the electromagnetic interaction is used to distinguish electrons from positrons*. Without this distinction, we would simply know that some muon decay products have positive helicity and some have negative helicity. The overall expectation value would be zero and there would be no evidence for parity violation. Again, the experiment of Wu et al. showed spatially asymmetric behaviour in the weak decay of ^{60}Co. Now anti-^{60}Co is expected to have the opposite asymmetry and so a statistical mixture of the two would have no asymmetry at all. But it is not possible to distinguish ^{60}Co from anti-^{60}Co using the weak interaction *alone* and thus a weak interaction eigenstate could well be just such a statistical mixture. It is only when the strong and electromagnetic interactions are present that the two can be distinguished and the asymmetry detected. Similar reasoning can be applied to all other cases. We conclude that parity violation can be observed only when the weak interaction is present together with the electromagnetic or strong interactions. For this reason, Lee (1966) has suggested that it might be useful to think of parity as being conserved in each class of interaction individually, but to say that the weak interaction parity operator differs from the parity operators for the strong and electromagnetic interactions.

2.3. Charge conjugation

The charge-conjugation operation is defined as that operation which replaces every particle in a system by its corresponding anti-particle. The properties inverted are charge, Q, hypercharge, Y, baryon number, B, and the two lepton numbers, L_e, L_μ. (Each of these will be discussed explicitly later in the book.) Thus the charge-conjugation operator, T, satisfies the following relations

$$TQT^{-1} = -Q, \qquad TYT^{-1} = -Y, \qquad TBT^{-1} = -B,$$

$$TL_eT^{-1} = -L_e, \qquad TL_\mu T^{-1} = -L_\mu. \tag{2.30}$$

Using eqns (2.30), it is possible to assign to every physical state a transformed state and it follows that charge conjugation is a unitary symmetry. It is also clear that it is discrete. The discussion given in Section 2.1 is therefore relevant.

The transformation of other observables under charge conjugation can be derived from eqns (2.30). Kinematic quantities, such as position, momentum, angular momentum, and helicity are left unchanged. But certain internal quantities which are defined in terms of Q, Y, B are inverted. These are strangeness, S, and the z component, I_z, of isospin

$$S = Y - B, \qquad I_z = Q - \tfrac{1}{2}Y. \tag{2.31}$$

The magnitude of the magnetic dipole moment is unchanged, but its direction is reversed.

Much of the reasoning which was used in the last section can be applied with only minor modification. First, let us treat charge conjugation as a symmetry principle. It asserts that to every physical state there can be assigned a charge-conjugate state such that the physics of the system remains unaltered. Consider an arbitrary non-interacting state. We require that it should be possible to find a charge-conjugate state which will have identical properties provided that all observables are transformed appropriately. In practice, given a particle with particular values of Q, Y, B, L_e, L_μ, it has always been possible to find a corresponding anti-particle with opposite values of these quantum numbers. The proton, for instance, has $Q = e$, $Y = B = 1$; the anti-proton has $Q = -e$, $Y = B = -1$. This part of the prediction, then, is always fulfilled. However, we shall see presently that it does not depend on charge conjugation as such. It can also be derived from the much weaker postulate of PCT. (See Section 2.5.) The prediction which does follow from charge conjugation but not from PCT is that charge conjugate states should have identical kinematic properties. This prediction is *not* always fulfilled. The neutrino, for instance, has fixed negative helicity. The anti-neutrino has fixed *positive* helicity. This immediately gives evidence that charge conjugation is not an exact symmetry of nature.

Now consider the predictions which can be made about interactions. Once again, they are given formally by eqns (1.139), (1.144), (1.145),

$$[H, T] = [U, T] = [S, T] = 0,$$

which now state that the operators describing the time development of any system must have the same form as those describing the time development of its charge conjugate. (Note that only an active formulation is possible, since we cannot examine a system in two 'charge-conjugate frames of reference'.) The predictions have very much smaller practical importance than those from parity since it is not often experimentally convenient to compare charge-conjugate states. Anti-^{60}Co, for instance, has not yet been produced!

Consider again the experiment of Culligan et al. (1959). This has already been used as evidence that parity is not an exact symmetry in muon decay. However, the main motive behind the experiment was to check one of the predictions of charge conjugation. It was performed at a time when parity violation had been discovered and it had become of interest to test the validity of other discrete symmetries. In fact, as we have seen, it showed that positrons from muon decay have positive helicity while electrons have negative helicity. This difference immediately establishes that charge conjugation is not an exact symmetry in these decays.

Next, consider charge conjugation as a conservation law or selection rule. The logic runs so closely parallel to that of parity that it can be dismissed briefly. We have seen that selection rules of this kind can be applied only to states which satisfy eqn (2.9), that is, to those which are invariant under the charge-conjugation operation except for a possible phase factor. It follows from eqns (2.30) that such states must have zero charge, hypercharge, baryon number, and lepton numbers.

Of course, few states satisfy these conditions and the selection rule has very few applications. However, a simple example to which it can be applied is the decay of π^0 into photons. The photon is an eigenstate of charge conjugation with eigenvalue -1 and it follows that an arbitrary n-photon state will also be an eigenstate and will have eigenvalue $(-1)^n$. We should therefore expect π^0 to decay into an odd number of photons or an even number of photons *but not both*. This prediction is fulfilled. The decay $\pi^0 \to 2\gamma$ is observed, but the decay $\pi^0 \to 3\gamma$ is not. (Duclos *et al.* 1965.)

Although charge-conjugation symmetry is of rather limited practical importance as a tool in particle physics research, it is nevertheless of considerable theoretical interest as representing the symmetry between the behaviour of matter and anti-matter. For this reason, much work has been done in determining the interactions to which it applies. There is good evidence that it is an exact symmetry for the strong interaction. (See for instance the review of Nilsson 1967.) Equally, the experiment of Culligan *et al.* and other similar experiments show that it is badly violated when the weak interaction is involved. Its status for the electromagnetic interaction, however, is still in some dispute. The history is worth recounting briefly. Until 1965, it had been assumed that existing evidence, such as that from the decay of π^0 into photons, was sufficient to establish that it was an exact symmetry for the electromagnetic interaction. In that year, Bernstein, Feinberg, and Lee (1965) pointed out that the evidence was in fact insufficient and in several instances quite misleading. For instance, it was known that the π^0 decay rate into three photons was less than that into two photons by a factor of about 4×10^{-4}. Bernstein *et al.* pointed out that this ratio could be explained quite satisfactorily by comparing the phase space available to the two decays without invoking charge-conjugation symmetry at all. It was not until the work of Duclos *et al.* (1965) that experiments were sufficiently accurate to be useful. The work of Bernstein *et al.* revived interest in charge conjugation and many further experiments were carried out. Most of these gave results consistent with exact charge-conjugation symmetry. Now, we have seen that this is not sufficient to establish that the symmetry is, in fact, exact. Each of the results could be dynamical in origin or could follow from some other quite different principle. However, the cumulative effect of a sequence of successful predictions has been to convince most physicists that any violation is at most a small one and the experimental status of charge conjugation is no longer of the highest interest.

2.4. Time reversal

The time-reversal operator is defined as that operator which reverses the direction of time. It is clearly a discrete symmetry and the discussion in Section 1.6 shows that it is anti-unitary and anti-linear. The transformation of physical observables under time reversal may be derived using the methods already applied to parity. Position, $\mathbf{r}$, and helicity, $\hat{\boldsymbol{\sigma}} \cdot \mathbf{p}$, are left unchanged

$$T\mathbf{r}T^{-1} = \mathbf{r}, \qquad T\hat{\boldsymbol{\sigma}} \cdot \hat{\mathbf{p}}T^{-1} = \hat{\boldsymbol{\sigma}} \cdot \hat{\mathbf{p}} \qquad (2.32)$$

but momentum, $\mathbf{p}$, angular momentum, $\mathbf{L}$, and intrinsic spin, $\boldsymbol{\sigma}$, are reversed

$$T\mathbf{p}T^{-1} = -\mathbf{p}, \qquad T\mathbf{L}T^{-1} = -\mathbf{L}, \qquad T\boldsymbol{\sigma}T^{-1} = -\boldsymbol{\sigma}. \qquad (2.33)$$

Most other observables are left unchanged.

In the present section, time reversal will be treated only as a symmetry principle. Since it is anti-unitary, it cannot lead to a conservation law, even in the limited sense discussed in Section 2.1. This is easily seen by remembering that it must satisfy eqn (1.153) rather than eqn (1.145) and thus that the reasoning used when deriving eqn (2.11) is not applicable. However, as we have seen, the squared operator, TT, does lead to an important superselection rule (cf. eqn (2.8)). The physical consequences of this will be described in Chapter 3, while in Section 4.7 the time-reversal operator will be constructed explicitly and the connection between TT and statistics will be derived.

As a symmetry principle, time reversal asserts that to every physical state there can be assigned a time-reversed state such that the physics of the system remains unaltered. Consider an arbitrary non-interacting state. We require that it should be possible to find a time-conjugate state which will have identical properties provided that they are measured in a time-reversed frame of reference. In practice, this imposes few constraints. It is always possible to reverse the direction of vector and axial vector quantities. Having found a proton with momentum, $\mathbf{p}$, and spin, $\boldsymbol{\sigma}$, for instance, it is always possible to find another proton with momentum, $-\mathbf{p}$, and spin, $-\boldsymbol{\sigma}$. Constraints arise only with observable scalar or pseudoscalar quantities which change sign under time reversal. Time-reversal invariance requires that these must have zero expectation value for any non-interacting state.

An important consequence of this rule is that no particle can have both an electric and a magnetic dipole moment. For, if it did,

$$\langle q^2 \boldsymbol{\sigma} \cdot \mathbf{r} \rangle \neq 0 \qquad (2.34)$$

where q is the electric charge, $\boldsymbol{\sigma}$ the spin vector of the magnetic dipole, and $\mathbf{r}$ the displacement vector of the electric dipole. This quantity changes sign under time reversal and so a non-zero expectation value would immediately give evidence that time reversal is not an exact symmetry of nature. In fact, no electric dipole moment has yet been detected for any particle and the current experimental limits are very low—a few times 10^{-23} e·cm for the neutron (see Baird et al. 1969). Unfortunately, this does not on its own establish time-reversal invariance. The pseudoscalar in eqn (2.34) also changes sign under parity and thus the electric dipole moment will be zero if *either* parity *or* time reversal are exact symmetries. Indeed, it will be non-zero only if time reversal and parity are simultaneously violated in the *same* part of the static Hamiltonian. The experimental evidence is perfectly consistent with a Hamiltonian made up of two parts, one of which is not invariant under parity and the other of which is not invariant under time reversal.

Next, consider the predictions which can be made about interactions. They were given formally in eqns (1.139), (1.150), (1.153):

$$[H, T] = 0, \qquad U = (TUT^{-1})^{\dagger}, \qquad S = (TST^{-1})^{\dagger}.$$

These equations state essentially that the laws governing the time development of a system must be the same in two time-conjugate frames of reference. Note that they are not the same as the equations which were used in discussing parity and charge conjugation, since time reversal is anti-unitary and inverts the order of initial and final states. Time-reversal symmetry leads to two experimental predictions for reactions. First, we observe that it relates the properties of two different physical systems which are set up so that one is the time inverse of the other. This is the *active formulation*, which we mentioned when discussing parity. Consider an interaction of the form

$$A + B \rightleftharpoons C + D. \tag{2.35}$$

If time reversal is an exact symmetry, then the magnitudes of the forward and reverse transition amplitudes should be equal. This prediction is known as *detailed balancing*. It is most readily applied to the strong interaction, and experimental tests have shown that in this case it is satisfied with high accuracy (Nilsson 1967). It is also satisfied in the electromagnetic interaction, but the experiments are more difficult and the accuracy is considerably lower. However, in the weak interaction the cross sections are so small that a pair of weak reactions of the form (2.35) has not yet been studied.

Secondly, consider a prediction which can be made about interactions in the *passive formulation*. An important special consequence of eqn (1.153) can be deduced *provided that the reaction amplitudes are sufficiently small*. This is that, if any scalar or pseudoscalar quantity which can be observed in the final state of a decay changes sign under time reversal, then its expectation value must be zero. For example, if $\mathbf{p_a}$, $\mathbf{p_b}$ are two momenta and $\boldsymbol{\sigma}$ is an angular momentum, then $\boldsymbol{\sigma} \cdot \mathbf{p_a} \times \mathbf{p_b}$ is a scalar quantity which changes sign under time reversal. Its expectation value must therefore be zero. By contrast, $\mathbf{p_a} \cdot \mathbf{p_b}$ and $\mathbf{p_a} \cdot \boldsymbol{\sigma}$ are respectively scalar and pseudoscalar quantities which do not change sign under time reversal. They may therefore have non-zero expectation values. We emphasize, however, that this prediction applies only to cases for which all parts of the reaction amplitude are very small. It applies to the pure weak interaction, but does not apply when either the strong or electromagnetic interaction is present.

In order to prove this result, write the operator, S, in the form

$$S \equiv I + \mathrm{i}t. \tag{2.36}$$

This equation should be considered as a *definition* of t. S is now divided into two parts—the identity operator, I, which leaves the system unchanged and a new operator, t, which induces transitions. If the transitions result from the weak interaction, then t will be very small. Now, by eqn (1.102), S is unitary.

$$\therefore \quad S^\dagger S = (I - \mathrm{i}t^\dagger)(I + \mathrm{i}t) = I,$$

$$\therefore \quad t - t^\dagger = \mathrm{i}t^\dagger t. \tag{2.37}$$

But, if t is very small, the right hand side of eqn (2.37) can be neglected compared with either term on the left hand side. It follows that

$$t = t^\dagger. \tag{2.38}$$

In physical terms, the condition used in passing from the exact eqn (2.37) to the approximate eqn (2.38) is that second order transitions can be neglected and hence that the reaction does not proceed through intermediate states. Now the condition that time reversal, T, should be an exact symmetry of the interaction is given by eqn (1.153)

$$S^\dagger = TST^{-1}$$

$$\therefore \quad I - \mathrm{i}t^\dagger = I - \mathrm{i}TtT^{-1}$$

$$\therefore \quad t^\dagger = TtT^{-1}, \tag{2.39}$$

where we have made use of the fact that T is anti-linear. Eqns (2.38), (2.39) give immediately

$$[t, T] = 0. \tag{2.40}$$

Thus, although S, T do not commute, t, T do commute provided that t is sufficiently small. Next, consider a specific transition between an initial state, ϕ, and a final state, $S\phi$. The part of the final state which differs from the initial state may be written

$$|\chi\rangle \equiv it|\phi\rangle. \tag{2.41}$$

χ is not normalized, but this will not affect the argument. Now let R be an operator corresponding to any scalar or pseudoscalar observable. Its expectation value in the final state will be proportional to

$$\langle\chi|R|\chi\rangle = \langle t\phi|R|t\phi\rangle$$
$$= \langle Tt\phi|TRT^{-1}|Tt\phi\rangle$$
$$= \langle tT\phi|TRT^{-1}|tT\phi\rangle \tag{2.42}$$

where the first step uses eqn (1.114) and the fact that the expectation value of R is real. The second step uses eqn (2.40). Consider the meaning of eqn (2.42). TRT^{-1} is the operator, R', obtained by operating on R with T (cf. eqn (1.133)). $T\phi$ is the initial state viewed in the time-inverse frame of reference. Since it is a stationary state, it will differ from ϕ only in that the direction of its spin will be opposite. But, if R is a scalar or pseudoscalar, then its expectation value will be independent of the direction of the spin of ϕ,

$$\therefore \quad \langle\chi|R|\chi\rangle = \langle t\phi|TRT^{-1}|t\phi\rangle$$
$$= \langle\chi|R'|\chi\rangle. \tag{2.43}$$

But, if R changes sign under time reversal, then R, R' have opposite expectation values. Both sides of eqn (2.43) must therefore be zero and the result is proved.

An example may help to make the point clear. In the decay

$$\mathrm{K}^+ \to \pi^0 + \mu^+ + \nu,$$

let $\mathbf{p}_\pi$, $\mathbf{p}_\mu$ be the momenta of π^0, μ^+ and let the muon spin be $\boldsymbol{\sigma}$. Were the muon to have a polarization component normal to the decay plane, we would have

$$\langle\boldsymbol{\sigma}\cdot(\mathbf{p}_\pi\times\mathbf{p}_\mu)\rangle \neq 0 \tag{2.44}$$

But, since this quantity changes sign under time reversal and *since the decay proceeds entirely by the weak interaction*, this would be direct evidence for time-reversal non-invariance. The effect has not been observed, but the experimental limits are poor (Fitch 1967). In contrast, consider the pair of reactions (2.25). The pseudoscalar quantity in eqn (2.26) changes sign under time reversal. Nevertheless, as we have already mentioned, this is *not* evidence for time-reversal non-invariance in either the production or the decay of Λ^0 since both involve the strong interaction. The production proceeds purely by the strong interaction and the decay is into strongly interacting particles, which may scatter from each other before they separate. In both cases, second order effects are possible and eqn (2.38) is invalid. These second order effects are known as *final-state interactions*.

It is instructive to compare this reasoning with the reasoning used when discussing parity (see Section 2.2). In the experiment of Wu *et al.* a non-zero expectation value for the pseudoscalar, $\boldsymbol{\sigma} \cdot \mathbf{p}$, is taken as direct evidence for parity violation without considering whether final-state interactions are involved. (As it happens, they are not.) Similarly, eqn (2.26) establishes that there is parity violation in either the production or the decay of Λ^0, although, as we have seen, final-state interactions are certainly involved and may be important. It should now be clear that the difference is due to the fact that parity commutes with the S-matrix (eqn (1.145)) while time reversal does not (eqn (1.153)). Eqn (1.145) is used directly in deriving eqn (2.24), which is therefore exact. But in deriving the analogous eqn (2.43) we are forced to use the *approximate* eqn (2.40). The latter holds only in the absence of final-state interactions. It is important to keep the difference between the predictions for the two types of symmetry clearly in mind.

This completes the discussion of the physical consequences which can be derived if time reversal is an exact symmetry. We finally summarize the evidence on the class of interactions for which these consequences hold. We have already seen that there is good evidence from detailed balancing that they hold for the strong interaction. There is no direct evidence that they are violated in the electromagnetic or weak interactions. However, indirect evidence can be derived from the *PCT* theorem. This states that the combined operation—parity, charge conjugation, and time reversal is an exact symmetry for all interactions. Thus, for the electromagnetic interaction, if parity is an exact symmetry and charge conjugation is violated, then time reversal will be violated by a corresponding amount. It is not yet clear whether these violations occur. Equally, since, as we shall see, the combined operation, PC, is not an exact symmetry for certain weak interactions, it follows that time reversal cannot be exact either. This point will be discussed in more detail in the next section.

2.5. The combined operations PC and PCT

It is clear that, since parity, charge conjugation, and time reversal are all discrete symmetry operations, then any two or, indeed, all three taken together will also form a discrete symmetry operation. If only parity and charge conjugation are included, then the composite symmetry will be unitary and will lead to a selection rule; but if time reversal is included, then the composite symmetry will be anti-unitary and will not lead to a selection rule. Of course, no new physics is introduced by considering combinations of symmetries each one of which, taken individually, is exact. The predictions which can be made will simply be a subset of the predictions which follow from the individual symmetries. However, we have seen that each discrete symmetry is exact for only a limited range of interactions. In this section, we consider composite symmetries which have wider validity than each of their components taken individually. Much of the reasoning is closely analogous to that used for the individual symmetries and can therefore be summarized very briefly.

First, consider the combined operation, PCT. This is made up from all three discrete symmetry operations taken together in any order. It has considerable theoretical importance since it can be shown to hold for *all* Lorentz invariant local field theories (Sakurai 1964). It should thus hold exactly for strong, electromagnetic, and weak interactions. Indeed, it is not clear how one would set up the formalism to describe a world in which it was not exact. Of course the corollary of the fact that it can be derived from fewer assumptions than the three separate discrete symmetries is that it imposes much less stringent conditions on physical phenomena. However, several of these conditions have been tested and are satisfied with high precision.

The transformation of physical observables under PCT may be derived by the usual methods. Linear momentum, $\mathbf{p}$, is left unchanged, but position, $\mathbf{r}$, angular momentum, $\mathbf{L}$, spin, $\boldsymbol{\sigma}$, helicity, $\hat{\boldsymbol{\sigma}} \cdot \hat{\mathbf{p}}$, charge, Q, hypercharge, Y, baryon number, B, and the lepton numbers, L_e, L_μ, all change sign. The PCT theorem asserts that to every physical state there can be assigned a PCT conjugate state such that the physics of the system is unaltered. This implies, for a non-interacting state, that to every particle in the state there can be assigned a corresponding anti-particle and that the properties of the two will be identical, provided that all observables are transformed appropriately. It thus resembles charge conjugation in that it essentially gives a prescription for deducing the properties of an anti-particle from those of the corresponding particle and, indeed, many of the predictions are the same. For instance, it asserts that the electric charges of charge-conjugate states must be equal and opposite, and that the masses must be equal. So does charge conjugation. But the assertion now has more significance. Charge conjugation is known to be seriously violated when the weak interaction is involved. Its predictions can therefore at best be accurate up to the level of weak corrections. PCT should be correct for *all* interactions. In fact, the mass equality has been verified to about one part in 10^{14} for K^0, $\overline{K}^0$ (Nilsson 1967). The most important difference between the two predictions is for helicity. Charge conjugation asserts that the helicities of the neutrino and anti-neutrino should be the same, PCT that they should be opposite. As we have seen, the latter is correct.

Next, consider the predictions which can be made about interactions. Since PCT is an anti-unitary symmetry, many of the ideas used when discussing time reversal are applicable. The relevant equations are (1.139), (1.150), (1.153). They state that the laws governing the time development of a system must be the same in two PCT conjugate frames of reference. In the active formulation, this implies that the magnitudes of the transition amplitudes

$$A + B \rightarrow C + D, \qquad \overline{C} + \overline{D} \rightarrow \overline{A} + \overline{B} \qquad (2.45)$$

must be equal (cf. eqn (2.35)). $\overline{A}$ is the anti-particle conjugate of A. In practice, this prediction is not useful since it is very difficult to find a pair of conjugate reactions of the form (2.45) which can be examined experimentally. A more useful rule can be derived in analogy with eqn (2.43). Like the latter, it holds only for the weak interaction. It states that, in the absence of final state interactions, the expectation value of any observable in two charge-conjugate decays will be identical provided that the operator corresponding to the observable is transformed appropriately.

Consider two examples. The experiment of Culligan *et al.* (1959) showed that the positrons from muon decay have positive helicity. Now helicity changes sign under PCT and hence, since the decay proceeds by the weak interaction, PCT predicts that electrons from muon decay should have negative helicity. They do. Similarly, if in K^+ decay the expectation value (2.44) were greater than zero, then PCT predicts that the analogous quantity for K^- decay would be less than zero. We remind the reader, however, that neither inequality has in fact been observed.

Finally, consider decay rates. Since PCT is anti-unitary, it will not commute with the S-matrix but will transform the latter to its hermitian conjugate. However, by eqn (2.40), PCT will commute with the t-matrix, *provided that there are no final-state interactions*. Thus the rates of two charge-conjugate weak decays will be identical. For example

$$\mathrm{K}^+ \to \mu^+ + \nu, \qquad \mathrm{K}^- \to \mu^- + \bar{\nu} \qquad (2.46)$$

are one such pair of decays. However, the position is rather more complicated if final-state interactions are present. Clearly, if they simply alter the kinematic state of the particles, then the total *rate* is not affected. But, if the particles interact in the final state to produce *different* particles, then PCT simply predicts that the *total* decay rate, into all states which can transform among themselves, is the same in two charge-conjugate modes. For instance, suppose that an initial state, ψ, can decay into either ϕ or χ and that ϕ, χ can change one to the other in the final state. Schematically, the possible interactions would look like this

$$\psi \to \phi \to \phi$$
$$\psi \to \chi \to \chi. \qquad (2.47)$$

Then PCT asserts that the rates of the *initial* reactions $\psi \to \phi$, $\psi \to \chi$ are the same as those of their charge conjugates. However, without more detailed information all it allows us to say about the *observed* rates is that the total decay rate of ψ into the two final states ϕ, χ is the same as that of $\bar{\psi}$ into $\bar{\phi}$, $\bar{\chi}$.

As an example, compare the decays

$$\mathrm{K}^+ \to \pi^+ + \pi^0, \qquad \mathrm{K}^- \to \pi^- + \pi^0. \qquad (2.48)$$

The pion pairs in the final state may scatter from each other, but no other states are accessible through the strong interaction. Hence to a first approximation the reaction rates are equal. However, by the *electromagnetic* interaction, it is possible to produce one or more photons. Thus, strictly speaking, PCT predicts only the equality of the total rates

$$\mathrm{K}^+ \to \pi^+ + \pi^0 + n\gamma, \qquad \mathrm{K}^- \to \pi^- + \pi^0 + n\gamma, \qquad (2.49)$$

where $n = 0, 1, 2, 3. \ldots$ In fact, the rate falls off rapidly as the number of photons increases and hence the rates (2.48) are equal to a good approximation.

This completes the discussion of PCT symmetry. We emphasize again that, as far as is known, it holds for *all* interactions. Its predictions are few, but highly important. However, where a prediction follows from both PCT and charge conjugation, it is important to remember that this will prevent it from being a useful test of the latter.

Now, consider the combined operation PC, where P stands for parity and C stands for charge conjugation. The reader will have noticed that in several cases violations of parity and charge conjugation are closely related. For instance, the fact that the neutrino has a definite helicity shows that parity cannot be an exact symmetry of nature, since the parity conjugate of the neutrino has opposite helicity. But the charge conjugate of the neutrino also has opposite helicity! Thus under the combined operation PC, the neutrino changes to the anti-neutrino and its helicity transforms correctly. Evidence of this sort led one to suspect that, although neither P nor C is an exact symmetry, the combined symmetry, PC, might well be exact. We therefore consider the predictions which this symmetry makes and the range of interactions for which these predictions are valid.

The predictions are closely similar to those of charge conjugation and PCT. First, consider PC as a symmetry principle. It asserts that to every physical state there can be assigned a PC conjugate state such that the physics of the system remains unaltered. Applied to a non-interacting state, it provides yet another prescription for deducing the properties of an anti-particle from those of its corresponding particle. It is easy to see that almost all these predictions will be identical with those of PCT. In particular, they give a correct account of the neutrino helicity. There is just one small but interesting difference. Consider the expectation value, $\langle q^2 \boldsymbol{\sigma} \cdot \mathbf{r} \rangle$, which was given in eqn (2.34). This is left invariant under PCT, but changes sign under PC. Hence these two symmetries give opposite predictions for any electric dipole moments. It follows that, if any particle is found to have a non-zero electric dipole moment and PCT is an exact symmetry, then PC is violated. Thus a non-zero electric dipole moment would provide evidence that *none* of P, T, PC are exact symmetries of nature. As we have seen, however, there is no evidence that any such dipole moments exist.

Next consider the predictions which can be made about interactions. The appropriate equations are (1.139), (1.144), (1.145) which now state that the operators describing the time development of any system must have the same form as those describing the time development of its PC conjugate. This statement can be applied directly, but a useful alternative rule which covers a number of cases can be derived in analogy with eqn (2.24). This rule states that the experimental values of any observable in two charge-conjugate decays are identical provided that the operator corresponding to the observable is transformed appropriately. Note that, since PC is a unitary symmetry, this rule is *exact*. It holds even if final-state interactions are present.

Consider some examples. The consequences of PC symmetry for the experiment of Culligan *et al.* are identical with those of PCT and need no further discussion. By contrast, the expectation value (2.44) changes sign under PCT but is left invariant under PC. Thus, if it is non-zero, the two symmetries cannot be satisfied simultaneously. However, as we have seen, there is as yet no experimental evidence that it is non-zero. Now consider decay rates. PC is unitary and hence, if it is an exact symmetry, it will commute with the S-matrix (cf. eqn (1.145)). Thus the decay rates in two charge conjugate modes will be identical *regardless* of whether final state interactions occur. This is a much stronger statement than the analogous prediction from PCT. It implies, for instance, that the two decays (2.49) have identical rates for *each* value of n. We return to this point presently.

Next, consider PC as a conservation law or selection rule. The logic is very similar to that of parity and charge conjugation. Selection rules of this kind can be applied only to states which satisfy eqn (2.9) and hence, in this case, to states which are invariant under PC except for a possible phase factor. They must have zero momentum, helicity, charge, hypercharge, baryon number and lepton number. Since few states satisfy these conditions, the selection rule has very few applications. One application, however, is of considerable importance. We have seen that, although there are large violations of P and C invariance when the weak interaction is involved, the combined symmetry, PC, has been exact in all cases studied. In neutral kaon decays, however, PC is approximately *but only approximately* satisfied. The first evidence for this surprising result was found by Christenson *et al.* (1964). They found that a definite state (the long lived neutral kaon) can decay into two different PC eigenstates—the predominantly $PC = -1$ three-pion state, plus a very small (0·2 percent) admixture of the pure $PC = +1$

two-pion state. As we saw in Section 2.1, this immediately gives evidence that PC is not an exact symmetry in this decay. The unfamiliar feature is that the violation is so small. In all other cases mentioned in this chapter, it has either been large or zero.

In order to understand the phenomenon, there have been many attempts to find other examples. So far, however, it has been entirely confined to neutral kaon decays. The experimental difficulties in making the search are formidable, not only because any violation is likely to be small but also because there are relatively few predictions which follow from PC but not PCT. Let us illustrate the point by considering the decays (2.49). With $n = 0$, these modes account for about 21 per cent of the charged kaon decay rate. With $n = 1$, the fraction is about 0·02 per cent and, with $n > 1$, it is still smaller. Neglecting the $n > 1$ decays, the PCT theorem implies

$$\text{Rate } (\text{K}^+ \to \pi^+\pi^0) - \text{Rate } (\text{K}^- \to \pi^-\pi^0) = \text{Rate } (\text{K}^- \to \pi^-\pi^0\gamma)$$
$$- \text{Rate } (\text{K}^+ \to \pi^+\pi^0\gamma).$$

$$(2.50)$$

PC makes the stronger prediction that both sides of eqn (2.50) should be zero. Thus a rate comparison could provide a test of PC. However, it is clear that the *fractional* difference in the $\pi\pi$ decay rates will be about 1000 times smaller than the *fractional* difference in the $\pi\pi\gamma$ decay rates. Attention should therefore be confined to the latter modes. But a little reflection will convince the reader that this is not the end of the story. The existence of final state interactions is a *necessary* condition if we are to observe PC violation, but it is by no means a *sufficient* one. PC violation requires a complex of decays of the form (2.47). One must have *both*

$$\text{K} \to \pi\pi \to \pi\pi\gamma \quad and \quad \text{K} \to \pi\pi\gamma. \qquad (2.51)$$

The former is known to occur by an 'inner bremsstrahlung' mode; the latter has yet to be detected. Furthermore, PCT implies that each of the decays, (2.51), taken on its own has the same amplitude for the two charge-conjugate modes. A total rate difference can be observed only if the two *interfere*. The conditions under which this could occur have been set out by Costa and Kabir (1967). It is far from clear that these conditions are satisfied. The $\pi\pi\gamma$ decays might well be entirely unsuitable as a test for PC. Possible rate differences have been discussed by Emmerson and Quirk (1970). And even assuming that the $\pi\pi\gamma$ decays could *in principle* test PC, the experimental difficulties are formidable. It is a measure of the extreme scarcity of good tests of PC that an experiment has in fact been mounted (Thresher 1971)! No results are available at the time of writing. The experimental information about PC violation is so limited that no clear theoretical understanding of the phenomenon has yet been possible. Although the only known violations are in the decay of neutral kaons, it could be that the violation is not in the weak interaction at all. Lee (1966) and his collaborators have suggested that it is a second order effect due ultimately to electromagnetic C violation. Its smallness is then no longer a puzzle since this is just what would be expected in an electromagnetic correction to the weak interaction. However, as we have seen, other searches for electromagnetic C violation have been unsuccessful and the hypothesis is now in some disfavour. Wolfenstein (1964) has suggested that the effect is due to a new CP non-invariant *superweak* interaction. Present evidence is consistent with this view. The subject has been well reviewed by Bell and Steinberger (1966), Vivargent (1967) and Kabir (1968).

The status of PC invariance for other interactions can be summarized briefly. For strong interactions it follows immediately from P and C invariance. Equally, for electromagnetic interactions, it is in doubt to exactly the same extent as C invariance. In neither case does it add anything to our understanding. However, where weak interactions are involved, the evidence is that although there are large violations of P and C invariances, invariance under the combined operation, PC, is usually exact. It is for this limited class of interactions that PC is really useful.

Problems

1. What statements can be made about the relative rates
   (a) $K^+ \to \pi^+ + \pi^+ + \pi^-$,
   (b) $K^+ \to \pi^+ + \pi^0 + \pi^0$,
   (c) $K^- \to \pi^- + \pi^- + \pi^+$,
   (d) $K^- \to \pi^- + \pi^0 + \pi^0$,
   assuming (i) charge conjugation, (ii) PC, (iii) PCT?

2. (a) What is the relation between helicity and plane and circular polarization for photons?
   (b) Suppose that the photons produced in the decays (2.49) are completely plane polarized in the decay plane. What is the relation connecting the amplitudes $\langle \pi\pi\gamma_+ |t| K^+ \rangle$ and $\langle \pi\pi\gamma_- |t| K^+ \rangle$, where the subscripts denote the helicity of the photon?
   (c) To what amplitude does PCT transform $\langle \pi\pi\gamma_+ |t| K^+ \rangle$?
   (d) Hence show that PCT invariance does not imply that $K^\pm \to \pi^+ + \pi^0 + \gamma$ have equal rates unless t is hermitian (cf. eqn (2.38)).

3

SUPERSELECTION RULES

THE remainder of the book will be concerned almost exclusively with symmetry principles which are related to conservation laws by eqn (1.157):

$$T = \exp[\mathrm{i}f(R)].$$

The discussion will rely heavily on the results derived in Chapter 1 and the principles will be classified according to the commutation rules that they obey. The present chapter deals with the simplest of all principles—the *superselection rules* (Wick *et al.* 1952). First, it explains what superselection rules are and how they differ from ordinary selection rules. Next, it lists the rules and deals with some of the consequences of their definition. Finally, it considers the limitations which they impose on the concept of intrinsic parity.

A superselection rule can be derived from any physical observable which is strictly conserved in all possible interactions. For a given system, the observable has the same value before and after *any* physical operation. Chapter 1 listed the types of operator used in quantum mechanics and explored some of the relations between them. In order to discuss the implications of superselection rules, it is necessary to consider in more detail which of these operators describe processes that occur physically. A typical experiment takes place in three stages. First, a system is prepared so that it has particular values of certain parameters. (A particle might be accelerated, for instance, to a given momentum.) Next, it is left undisturbed for a time during which an interaction may occur. Finally, certain quantities are measured. In the first and final stages, the observer interferes with the system and the crucial physical operations are *measurements*. The corresponding operators are denoted R. In the middle stage, the observer does not interfere with the system and the crucial physical operation is *time development*. As we have seen, this can always be described using the S-matrix although it is sometimes convenient to formulate the theory using the Hamiltonian, H. The third type of operator introduced in Chapter 1 is the symmetry operator, T. This is used to make statements about a system, but it does not correspond to an operation which is actually carried out physically. The definition of superselection rules says nothing about symmetry operators. We shall therefore confine our attention to the operators R, S, H.

Consider some observable, R. We require that the measured value of some superselection observable, R', should be the same before and after R is measured. The condition that this is so is easily derived. Consider an arbitrary state, ϕ, and suppose that a measurement is made of R'. This must yield an eigenvalue, r'_j say, of R'. Repeated measurements of R' will give the same result. Thus, after the measurement, ϕ has become an eigenstate, ψ'_j say, of R'. Now suppose that R is measured. This measurement will leave an eigenstate, ψ_k say, of R with eigenvalue r_k. But, if the value of R' is unchanged, this state must also be an eigenstate of R' with eigenvalue r'_j. Hence it must always be possible to express any state as a linear combination of simultaneous eigenstates of R, R'. As we saw in Chapter 1, this implies that it must be possible to diagonalize R, R' simultaneously and they must therefore *commute*. Conversely, if they commute it is obvious that the eigenvalue of R' will not be changed by a measurement of R. The condition is therefore both necessary and sufficient.

$$[R, R'] = 0. \tag{3.1}$$

It follows from this not only that any observable, R, will have zero matrix elements between any two states with different values of R', but also that R' will have zero matrix element between any two states with different eigenvalues of any other observable, R.

Now consider the time development operators, S, H. The condition that some observable, R, should be conserved is given by eqns (1.90), (1.107). R must commute with S and H. Some quantities are conserved for only a limited class of interactions. Isospin, for instance, is conserved in the strong interaction but not in the electromagnetic or weak interactions. Other quantities, such as momentum, are conserved in all interactions. Now any conservation law, even if it is valid for only a limited class of interactions, leads to a selection rule. It states that transitions between certain states are impossible by certain interactions. The operator corresponding to the observable commutes with some parts of the S-matrix (for instance the part corresponding to the strong interaction) and with some Hamiltonians and probably also with some other observables as well. However, the operator, R', corresponding to superselection rules must satisfy eqns (1.90), (1.107), (3.1) *without restriction*. They must commute with *all* S, H, R.

An example may help to make the distinction clear. Momentum, **p**, is conserved in all interactions. The corresponding operator therefore commutes with all S, H and leads to an important selection rule. However, it follows from the uncertainty principle that it does not commute with the position operator, **r**. Any measurement of **r** changes the value of **p**. Thus **p** cannot lead to a superselection rule. Similarly energy, E, although strictly conserved, does not lead to a super-selection rule since it does not commute with time.

The most important observables which lead to superselection rules are

1. Electric charge Q

It is important to remember that there are two quite separate ways in which electric charge can be measured and its conservation checked. First, there are the conventional methods using electric and magnetic fields. Secondly, one could define the charge of the proton and neutron to be $+e$, 0 respectively, and then examine a number of reactions to see whether charges could be assigned to all particles in a consistent way. The importance of the first method is that it can be applied quite independently of any other selection rules which may operate. It is therefore possible to define the consequences of charge conservation without any danger that they will be confused with the consequences of, say, baryon and lepton conservation.

2. Baryon number B

This is an extension of the idea of atomic mass number in nuclear physics. It is defined only for strongly interacting particles (*hadrons*) and for each state it can be determined only by assuming baryon conservation. The proton and neutron are each assigned baryon number one and hence, by examining various reactions, it is easy to assign a baryon number to every physical state. The statement that B is strictly conserved in all interactions is equivalent to the statement that this can be done without ambiguity. Almost all hadrons which are of interest have $B = 0$ or ± 1. Those with $B = 1$ are called *baryons*, those with $B = -1$ *antibaryons*, and those with $B = 0$ *mesons*.

3. Lepton numbers L_e, L_μ

These are the analogous quantities for the non strongly interacting particles (*leptons*). The electron is assigned $L_e = 1$ and it can then be shown experimentally that the positron and electron antineutrino have $L_e = -1$ while the electron neutrino has $L_e = 1$. Similarly, the negative muon and muon neutrino have $L_\mu = 1$ while the positive muon and muon antineutrino have $L_\mu = -1$.

4. Statistics

Conservation of statistics implies that a state with integral spin cannot change into a state with half integral spin and vice versa. It was mentioned in the last chapter that the corresponding superselection operator is the square of the time-reversal operator.

None of these rules is seriously in question at present and references to the relevant experiments can be found in the literature (e.g. Sakurai 1964). (Note particularly the evidence, Danby *et al.* 1962, that muon and electron numbers are separately conserved.) Considered simply as conservation laws, the superselection rules have rather obvious consequences. However, they are defined in a much more sweeping fashion than ordinary selection rules and some of the predictions which follow from their definition are far from obvious. We shall consider these predictions in turn.

First, the definition states that a superselection rule is derived from an observable which is unchanged in all physical operations. The operations were classified according to whether an observer does or does not interfere with the system. Symmetry operations were not included because they are not in fact carried out physically. However, it happens that a large number of symmetry operators can be expressed in the form (1.157) where R corresponds to an observable. It immediately follows from eqns (3.1), (1.136) that all superselection operators, R', will be invariant under such symmetry operations. For instance, all superselection operators are invariant under spatial translations and rotations. There are two main exceptions. The discrete symmetries *cannot* be expressed in the form (1.157). Therefore, one should not be surprised to find that charge, baryon number, and the two lepton numbers all change sign under charge conjugation (cf. eqns (2.30)). Rotations about the x and y axes in isospin space can be expressed in the form (1.157) but, as we shall see in Chapter 4, R does not then correspond to an observable. Therefore, one should not be surprised to find that charge is changed by such rotations.

Secondly, consider superselection rules as symmetry principles. Remember that the basic quantum mechanical equations (1.1), (1.8), (1.9), etc. do not determine an absolute phase for the state functions. Measurement of transition probabilities, eqn (1.9), and of the matrix elements of certain physical operators, H, S, R, will usually give *relative* phases. But for any complete orthonormal set of basis states, ψ_j, one phase can be chosen arbitrarily without affecting the physics. But now suppose that two states are separated by a superselection rule so that no transition whatever is possible between them. In this case it will be impossible to make a measurement to compare their phases and so the phase of each can be chosen arbitrarily without affecting the physics. This can be put more formally using eqn (1.157). The symmetry principle corresponding to any superselection rule implies invariance under an arbitrary change of relative phase between any two states with different quantum numbers of the superselection operator. For instance, the phase differences between states of charge 0, e, $2e$, . . . , will be completely indeterminate. (This is in fact an example of the gauge invariance in electrodynamics.) Thus the superselection rules have the effect of dividing the physical Hilbert space into *incoherent* subspaces labelled by different values of the superselection quantum numbers. A linear combination of states with different superselection quantum numbers would be incoherent and so could not correspond to a definite physical state. It follows that *any* definite physical state must be an eigenstate of *all* superselection operators.

Finally consider the limitations which superselection rules impose on the concept of intrinsic parity. We saw in Chapter 2 that the whole scheme for comparing the parities of two states, ϕ, χ, depends on the assumption that there is at least one transition, S, which allows ϕ to change into χ (eqn (2.2)). One then considers a parity-conserving transition, S', and observes whether or not *this* transition allows ϕ to change into χ. But if ϕ, χ have different superselection quantum numbers then no transition whatever can take place between them. There is thus no direct way in which relative parities can be determined. Of course, this is not the end of the story. There are also *indirect* ways in which parity can be determined. For instance, if a proton has intrinsic parity, β, then a two-proton state with orbital angular momentum, l, has parity $\beta^2(-1)^l$. Assuming that β can take only the values ± 1, (eqn (2.16)), this reduces to $(-1)^l$. Using arguments of this sort, it is possible to determine the parity of any multi-proton state. (Compare this with the argument about phases. Defining a phase for an arbitrary one-proton state tells us nothing whatever about the phase of a two- or three-proton state.) A second method uses reactions of the form

$$A + B \rightarrow C + D. \tag{3.2}$$

If this is *possible* by a parity-conserving reaction (that is, if the various selection rules are satisfied) and the parities of A, B, C are known, then the parity of D can be determined. In practice, a small number of intrinsic parities are *defined* in a theoretically convenient way and the rest can then be deduced. These definitions can be made in a number of different ways. The conventional ones are discussed below.

Let us start by defining the intrinsic parity of the proton as $+1$. Suppose now that we want to determine the intrinsic parity of the neutron. The neutron and proton have different charges and thus there is no direct way in which their relative parities can be determined. But a little reflection will convince the reader that there is no indirect way either! It is therefore necessary to *define* the intrinsic parity of the neutron. This is taken to be positive too, but physics would not be altered if another definition were used. It is now possible to determine the intrinsic parities of the anti-proton and anti-neutron *experimentally* using the reactions

$$p + p \rightarrow p + p + p + \bar{p},$$

$$p + p \rightarrow p + p + n + \bar{n}. \tag{3.3}$$

Similarly, as we saw in Chapter 2, the parity of the π^- can be determined. Also the reactions

$$p + p \rightarrow p + p + \pi^0,$$

$$p + p \rightarrow p + n + \pi^+, \tag{3.4}$$

can be used to determine the parities of π^0, π^+. More generally, having defined the parities of proton and neutron, it is possible to set up a state with any combination of charge, baryon number, and statistics that occurs in nature. Thus two definitions are sufficient to deal with the limitations imposed by the superselection rules on the concept of intrinsic parity.

Next consider the Λ. This decays into a proton and pion and therefore at first sight it seems possible to determine its parity in terms of the p, n parities. However, here a new snag arises. The decay proceeds by the weak interaction and so parity is not conserved. Nor can any parity-conserving reaction of the form (3.2) be used since the Λ has strangeness -1 while p, n, π all have strangeness zero. As we shall see in Chapter 5, strangeness is conserved in *all* those reactions which conserve parity. It therefore imposes limitations of the same sort as those imposed by the superselection rules. It follows that the parity of the Λ must also be chosen by definition. It is defined to be positive. No other selection rules are important in this context. Using the three definitions (p, n, Λ), the intrinsic parities of all other hadrons can be determined.

Notice that we have introduced three classes of intrinsic parity. In the largest class, parity depends on the definitions of p, n, Λ parities. In the second class, parity can be determined using only the convention (2.16). The two-neutron final state in the interaction (2.28) was an example from this class. In the final class, parity can be determined making no conventional assumptions whatever. The π^0 is an example from this class. Using the reaction (3.4), the parity of the π^0 can be determined without even assuming that the proton parity is real (cf. eqn (2.16)). A little reflection will convince the reader that states from this last class must have integral spin and zero charge, baryon number, lepton numbers and strangeness. States from the second class must have integral spin and even charge, baryon number, lepton numbers and strangeness.

This completes the discussion of intrinsic parities. Using these principles, the reader should have no difficulty in deciding how to determine the parity of any physical state.

Problems

1. What conventional assumptions must be made in order to assign intrinsic parities to Σ^0, K^0, ρ^0, ρ^+, η?

2. The leptons are not strongly interacting. Could one use the electromagnetic interaction in order to assign intrinsic parities to them? If so, how many definitions would be needed?

4

ANGULAR MOMENTUM AND ISOSPIN

ANGULAR momentum has been the subject of several admirable texts. (See, for example, Rose 1957, Edmonds 1957, Brink and Satchler 1968.) These books provide a detailed account of the ideas underlying angular momentum and of its application to physical systems. The present chapter covers part of the same ground. However the emphasis lies on the basic ideas and elementary formalism rather than on the details of the applications. Moreover, one of the aims of the book is to point out the relationships between the fundamental physics of various symmetry principles, and in this plan angular momentum occupies a pivotal position. For this reason, there are many cross references to other symmetry principles and, while angular momentum and isospin provide the basic theme of the chapter, a large part of the material lies outside the scope of the more conventional specialized texts. Our discussion falls into three main sections. First, it compares the commutation relations which are satisfied by the angular momentum operators with those of the superselection rules and the canonically conjugate pairs of variables. Secondly, it develops the algebra of angular momentum from these commutation relations and explains why it is identical with the algebra of isospin. In order to do this, it is necessary to introduce the tensor formalism of SU_2. This is particularly useful since a large part of the algebra can be carried over to the subsequent treatment of SU_3 and SU_6. Thirdly, it deals with two discrete symmetries—G-parity and time reversal. The operators for both of these are derived directly from the angular momentum operators.

4.1. The generators of continuous transformations

An important result derived at the end of Chapter 1 was that to every hermitian operator, R, it is possible to associate a family of unitary operators, T, given by the equation

$$T = \exp[if(R)], \tag{4.1}$$

where $f(R)$ is any real function of R (cf. eqn (1.157)). If R corresponds to an observable, then T corresponds to an associated symmetry operation and, if R is conserved, then T is an exact symmetry. The particular form, eqn (4.1), was chosen to emphasize that the relationship between the two is not unique. However, in what follows we shall note that if R is observable and $f(R)$ is known then $f(R)$ is also observable. For this reason, in the interests of simplicity, we shall write eqn (4.1) as

$$T = e^{iR}, \tag{4.2}$$

where R is now an hermitian operator corresponding to any real known function of an observable.

In the present section, we shall be concerned with continuous transformations. That is, T must be a function of parameters which vary continuously in a certain region. Most symmetry operators to be considered from now on fall into this class. Continuous transformations have the special property that it is possible to make up any finite transformation, T, out of a set of infinitesimal steps each of the form

$$T(\delta) = e^{i\delta R} = I + i\delta R + 0(\delta^2), \tag{4.3}$$

where δ is infinitesimal. (It is a *number*, not an operation on R.) When δ is sufficiently small, the last term in eqn (4.3) can be neglected. We saw in Chapter 1 that if R is hermitian then T is unitary. Conversely, if T is continuous and unitary then it is easy to shown that R is hermitian. Because of this special reciprocal relationship, R is referred to as the *generator* of T. It follows that every observable is the generator of a symmetry operation, and conversely that the generators of any continuous symmetry operation can usually be chosen to correspond in a simple way to physical observables. Of course, T may depend on more than one parameter. In this case there will be several independent generators

$$T(\delta) = I + i\delta \sum_j a_j R_j, \tag{4.4}$$

where the R_j are generators and the a_j are expansion coefficients. Clearly, a complete description of any continuous symmetry operation may be obtained from the properties of its generators. In fact, it turns out that a very large amount of information can be obtained simply from the *commutation relations* of the generators. Working with commutation relations not only simplifies the algebra but also makes it possible to cast the theory in a form which is independent of the choice of basis states. The explicit form of quantum mechanical operators depends on the choice of basis states. The commutation relations do not.

The importance of commutation relations has already been stressed. We have seen that the conditions that an observable should be conserved, and that a unitary symmetry operation should be exact, can be expressed in terms of commutation relations. We have also examined one class of observables which can be distinguished solely by their commutation relations. The superselection operators commute not only with all S-matrices and Hamiltonians but also with *all other observables*. From this fact and this fact alone it was possible to derive all their special properties.

A slightly more complicated case is that of a pair of observables for which the commutator is a constant, α say,

$$[R_1, R_2] = \alpha I. \tag{4.5}$$

The fact that R_1, R_2 are hermitian imposes a constraint on α. Taking the hermitian conjugate of eqn (4.5) and using eqn (1.53)

$$[R^\dagger_1, R^\dagger_2] = -\alpha^* I. \tag{4.6}$$

The left hand sides of eqns (4.5), (4.6) are equal and it follows that α is pure imaginary. Let us write it as ia where a is real. Now suppose that R_1 is an observable with continuous eigenvalues and that R_2 is the generator of a continuous symmetry operation, T. Consider the behaviour of R_1 under an infinitesimal transformation, $T(\delta)$.

$$R'_1 = T(\delta)R_1T(\delta)^{-1} = (I+i\delta R_2)R_1(I-i\delta R_2)$$
$$= R_1-i\delta[R_1, R_2] = R_1+\delta aI. \tag{4.7}$$

The eigenvalues of R'_1 differ from those of R_1 by δa. Hence, if R_1, R_2 are two observables which satisfy eqn (4.5) and R_1 is continuous then R_2 is the generator of a translation in R_1 (a symmetry operation). Conversely, if T is a continuous symmetry operation which produces a translation in R_1, then any hermitian operator, R_2, which satisfies eqn (4.5) is a generator of T. Conservation of R_2 is equivalent to invariance under a small displacement in R_1. Thus the commutator of two observables can give important and interesting results even when it is not zero.

Now it is of course well known that pairs of canonically conjugate operators satisfy equations of the form (4.5). The important examples are

1. Position, z, and momentum, $\mathbf{p}_z$

$$[z, \mathbf{p}_z] = \left[z, -i\hbar\frac{\partial}{\partial z}\right] = i\hbar I, \tag{4.8}$$

where we have used the standard operator substitution for momentum. This immediately tells us that the momentum operator generates a small displacement in position. Conservation of momentum is equivalent to invariance under spatial translation.

2. *Time, t, and energy, E*

$$[t, E] = \left[t, i\hbar\frac{\partial}{\partial t}\right] = -i\hbar I, \qquad (4.9)$$

where we have used the standard operator substitution for energy. Conservation of energy implies a Hamiltonian which is constant in time.

3. *Rotation, θ_z, about the z axis and angular momentum, L_z, about the same axis*

Angular momentum has the form

$$\mathbf{L} = \mathbf{r} \times \mathbf{p} \qquad (4.10)$$

$$\therefore \quad [\theta_z, L_z] = -i\hbar\left[\tan^{-1}\frac{y}{x}, x\frac{\partial}{\partial y} - y\frac{\partial}{\partial x}\right] = -i\hbar I. \qquad (4.11)$$

Hence the angular momentum operator generates a small rotation and conservation of angular momentum is equivalent to invariance under rotation. The classical analogues of each of these results should be familiar to the reader.

The commutation relations satisfied by the R_j are also useful when classifying symmetry operators of the form (4.4). If the R_j commute then any finite transformation, T, can always be expressed as the product of several transformations, T_j, each of which depends on only one R_j

$$T = \prod_j R_j \qquad (4.12)$$

No T_j need be used more than once and the order in which they are applied is immaterial. The properties of each T_j can thus be considered independently. For instance, a translation in three dimensional space can always be expressed as the product of three translations taken in any order, one parallel to each of the axes. If, however, the R_j do *not* commute then a much more complicated and interesting situation results. An example is considered in the next section.

4.2. Angular momentum

This section develops the basic algebra of angular momentum. Starting from the definition (4.10) it sets up the commutation relations between the Cartesian components of angular momentum. It then considers the pure angular momentum eigenstates and their behaviour under rotation. Next it considers the coupling between two angular momentum vectors and describes how the Clebsch–Gordan coefficients may be calculated. Finally, it introduces a more explicit formalism for angular momentum states and operators. This is based on the vector and matrix algebra developed in Chapter 1. However, it is argued that it has certain shortcomings and that it does not take advantage of some of the simplifying features of angular momentum theory. The notation is both too cumbersome and too general for many purposes. A more satisfactory formalism is developed in the following section.

Angular momentum is a familiar classical concept. It is an axial vector with three Cartesian components. Each of these is the generator of rotations about one of the coordinate axes. In both classical and quantum mechanics the theory is developed starting from eqn (4.10). In both cases, too, conservation of angular momentum is equivalent to invariance under spatial rotations. However there, for the most part, the resemblance ends. In classical mechanics most of the emphasis is on angular momentum considered as a dynamical variable that satisfies a conservation law. Each component of angular momentum is separately observable and the measurement is made directly in terms of position and momentum. In quantum mechanics, however, only one Cartesian component is observable (see below), and the methods for measurement are indirect. One may for instance measure angular distributions or observe what happens when the spatial symmetry is disturbed (as in the Zeeman effect). In all these cases one is studying the behaviour of systems under spatial rotations. The emphasis is thus on the spatial *symmetry* properties rather than on conservation of a dynamical variable. Of course, both aspects are present, but the reader will find the discussion much clearer if he remembers that an important change of emphasis has occurred in passing from classical physics to quantum mechanics.

Let us start from eqn (4.10) and make the usual operator substitution for momentum. It is immediately clear that the three components of angular momentum do not commute. For instance

$$[L_x, L_y] = -\hbar^2 \left[y\frac{\partial}{\partial z} - z\frac{\partial}{\partial y}, \ z\frac{\partial}{\partial x} - x\frac{\partial}{\partial z} \right]$$

$$= \hbar^2 \left(x\frac{\partial}{\partial y} - y\frac{\partial}{\partial x} \right) = i\hbar L z. \tag{4.13}$$

Eqn (4.13) remains true under cyclic permutations of the L_j. This result has been derived using the properties of orbital angular momentum. However, L_x, L_y, L_z are also the *generators of infinitesimal rotations*. Since rotational invariance is being stressed, it is useful to generalize the treatment by introducing three quantities, J_x, J_y, J_z, which satisfy

$$[J_x, J_y] = i\hbar J_z, \tag{4.14}$$

but which are now considered to be the generators of infinitesimal rotations, without any *necessary* connection with orbital angular momentum. The whole discussion can then be kept much more general. In addition to orbital angular momentum, we can allow particles to have an *intrinsic spin* which is connected with their behaviour under spatial rotations rather than with any directly observable dynamical properties.

Now, since J_x, J_y, J_z do not commute, any given state, ϕ say, can be an eigenstate of at most one of them. Let us choose this one to be J_z and let its eigenvalue be $m\hbar$.

$$J_z|\phi\rangle = m\hbar|\phi\rangle. \tag{4.15}$$

But we can also construct an operator

$$J^2 \equiv J_x J_x + J_y J_y + J_z J_z, \tag{4.16}$$

which commutes with *all* the J_i. It follows that ϕ can also be an eigenstate of J^2 with eigenvalue $x\hbar^2$, say.

$$J^2|\phi\rangle = x\hbar^2|\phi\rangle. \tag{4.17}$$

Angular momentum eigenstates are *defined* as those states which are simultaneously eigenstates of J_z, J^2. Now in order to understand the behaviour of ϕ when operated on by J_x, J_y, it is convenient to introduce two linear combinations

$$J_\pm \equiv J_x \pm iJ_y. \tag{4.18}$$

Consider the state ϕ' defined by

$$|\phi'\rangle \equiv J_+|\phi\rangle. \tag{4.19}$$

We have

$$J_z|\phi'\rangle = (J_zJ_x + iJ_zJ_y)|\phi\rangle$$

$$= J_+(J_z + \hbar I)|\phi\rangle = (m+1)\hbar|\phi'\rangle, \tag{4.20}$$

where we have used eqn (4.14). But, since J_+, J^2 commute,

$$J^2|\phi'\rangle = x\hbar^2|\phi'\rangle. \tag{4.21}$$

Thus ϕ' is a *new simultaneous eigenstate* of J_z, J^2. J_+ increases the eigenvalue of J_z by one unit while leaving the eigenvalue of J^2 unchanged. It is called a *stepping* or *ladder operator*. Another useful relation may be obtained by considering

$$\langle\phi'|\phi'\rangle = \langle\phi|J_+^{\dagger}J_+|\phi\rangle = \langle\phi|J^2 - J_z^2 - J_z\hbar|\phi\rangle$$

$$= (x - m^2 - m)\hbar^2\langle\phi|\phi\rangle, \tag{4.22}$$

where we have used eqns (4.14–19) and the fact that J_x, J_y are hermitian. ϕ' is not normalized. However, since its magnitude, like that of any other state function, must be greater than or equal to zero, it follows that

$$x \geqslant m(m+1). \tag{4.23}$$

This has important consequences. It means that m must have an upper bound, j say, and that the stepping operation, (4.19), cannot be continued indefinitely. Since eqn (4.22) is true without restriction, there must exist a ϕ_j such that

$$\langle\phi_j|\phi_j\rangle \neq 0, \tag{4.24}$$

but

$$\langle\phi'_j|\phi'_j\rangle = 0 \tag{4.25}$$

$$\therefore \quad x = j(j+1). \tag{4.26}$$

The quantum number, j, is not only the largest value which can be taken by m but also gives x by eqn (4.26). Similarly, using the stepping operator, J_-, it can be shown that $-j$ is the *smallest* value which can be taken by m.

$$|m| \leqslant j. \tag{4.27}$$

But, since the stepping operators change m by integral steps, it follows that the difference, $2j$, between its greatest and smallest values must also be integral. Thus j can take values $0, \frac{1}{2}, 1, \ldots$, and m can take the $2j+1$ values between $-j$ and j. This conclusion is derived using only eqn (4.14). Of course, it is well known that eigenstates of orbital angular momentum must satisfy an additional restriction. Their state functions must be single-valued at all points and this implies that the quantum number, l, can take only *integral* values. This restriction does not limit the quantum numbers s, j describing intrinsic spin and total angular momentum. s, j can both take integral or half integral values.

Equations (4.22), (4.26) also allow us to make a more explicit statement about the normalization in eqn (4.19). Let us write a normalized angular momentum eigenstate with quantum numbers j, m as $|j, m\rangle$. Then

$$J_+|j, m\rangle = e^{i\alpha}[j(j+1) - m(m+1)]^{\frac{1}{2}}|j, m+1\rangle, \qquad (4.28)$$

where α is real. By an analogous argument

$$J_-|j, m\rangle = e^{-i\alpha}[j(j+1) - m(m-1)]^{\frac{1}{2}}|j, m-1\rangle. \qquad (4.29)$$

Note that eqns (4.20), (4.22) are *invariant* under a change in α. α can therefore be chosen by convention. The usual convention sets it to zero and is part of the *Condon and Shortley phase convention*. It asserts that states with the same values of j but different values of m are kept in phase by the stepping operators.

So far, we have defined angular momentum eigenstates as simultaneous eigenstates of J_z, J^2. It is interesting to consider how such states behave under a rotation. We have already remarked that the operators J_x, J_y, J_z are the generators of spatial rotations. Specifically, eqns (4.7), (4.11) imply that $J_z\delta/\hbar$ changes θ_z to $\theta_z - \delta$. That is, it rotates any state, ϕ say, by δ radians in the *negative direction* about the z axis. Hence comparing eqns (4.2), (4.3), the symmetry operator

$$T_z(\alpha) \equiv \exp(-i\alpha J_z/\hbar), \qquad (4.30)$$

produces a finite rotation by α radians in the *positive direction* about the z axis. Now any finite rotation can be expressed as the product of three separate rotations—first a rotation by an angle γ about the z axis, then a rotation by an angle β about the y axis, and finally a rotation by an angle α about the z axis again. Hence the most general rotation operator can be written

$$T(\alpha, \beta, \gamma) = \exp(-i\alpha J_z/\hbar) \exp(-i\beta J_y/\hbar) \exp(-i\gamma J_z/\hbar); \qquad (4.31)$$

α, β, γ are known as the *Euler angles*. Since J_y, J_z do not commute, the order in which these rotations are made is important. Note that T has here been defined so that it rotates any state, ϕ, by the Euler angles α, β, γ. It could, equivalently, be taken to rotate the *coordinate system* by $-\alpha, -\beta, -\gamma$.

When describing the directional properties of an angular momentum state, another useful concept is the *polarization vector*, **P**, defined by

$$\mathbf{P} = \langle \mathbf{J} \rangle / j, \qquad (4.32)$$

where the angle brackets as usual denote the expectation value. If $|\mathbf{P}| = 1$, the state is said to be fully polarized. If $|\mathbf{P}| < 1$, it is said to be partially polarized. The magnitude of the polarization vector is, of course, unchanged by spatial rotations.

Next, consider the addition of two angular momenta, $\mathbf{j}_1, \mathbf{j}_2$ say, to produce a resultant angular momentum $\mathbf{j}$. The associated operator equation will be

$$\mathbf{J} = \mathbf{J}_1 + \mathbf{J}_2 \qquad (4.33)$$

where $\mathbf{J}_1$ refers to $\mathbf{j}_1$, $\mathbf{J}_2$ to $\mathbf{j}_2$ and $\mathbf{J}$ to $\mathbf{j}$. Now, since the three Cartesian components of angular momentum are not simultaneously well defined, it follows that we cannot use the normal rules for vector addition. The maximum amount of physical information which can be obtained for each angular momentum vector is given by the quantum numbers j, m. There are thus six operators which correspond to possible observables $-J_1{}^2, J_{1z}, J_2{}^2, J_{2z}, J^2, J_z$. Any two-angular-momentum state can be expressed as a linear combination of eigenstates of a maximal set of commuting operators chosen from amongst these six (cf. discussion in Chapter 1). Now, since $\mathbf{J}_1, \mathbf{J}_2$ refer to different systems, each component of one commutes with each component of the other. From this it is easy to show that most of the six operators commute amongst themselves. There is one exception. J^2 does *not* commute with J_{1z}, J_{2z}. Hence, while it is possible to find eigenstates of J^2 and eigenstates of J_{1z}, J_{2z}, it is not possible to find simultaneous eigenstates of both. This gives us a choice of two sets of basis states, one composed of simultaneous eigenstates of $J_1{}^2, J_{1z}, J_2{}^2, J_{2z}, J_z$ and the other composed of simultaneous eigenstates of $J_1{}^2, J_2{}^2, J^2, J_z$. In the first, the emphasis is on the constituent vectors. In the second, it is on the total vector. In describing the addition of two angular momenta, the problem is to convert from one basis to the other (cf. eqn (1.22)). Hence, indicating a state by its relevant quantum numbers we can write

$$|j, m\rangle = \sum_{m_1, m_2} C(j_1, j_2, j; m_1, m_2, m) |j_1, m_1\rangle |j_2, m_2\rangle. \qquad (4.34)$$

The expansion coefficients, $C(j_1, j_2, j; m_1, m_2, m)$, are called *Clebsch–Gordan* coefficients. They will be zero unless certain constraint equations are satisfied. It follows from eqn (4.33) that

$$|j_1 - j_2| \leqslant j \leqslant j_1 + j_2, \qquad m = m_1 + m_2; \qquad (4.35)$$

and from eqn (4.27) that

$$|m_1| \leqslant j_1, \qquad |m_2| \leqslant j_2, \qquad |m| \leqslant j. \qquad (4.36)$$

Within these limits, the Clebsch–Gordan coefficients are calculated by repeated use of stepping operators and normalization. This is a somewhat messy procedure in the general case (Condon and Shortley 1935) and for our present purpose the method can be sufficiently indicated by a special example.

Suppose that $j_1 = 1$ and $j_2 = \frac{1}{2}$. Then Table 4.1 shows the values of the other quantum numbers which are allowed by eqns (4.35), (4.36).

TABLE 4.1

m	j	m_1	m_2
$\frac{3}{2}$	$\frac{3}{2}$	1	$\frac{1}{2}$
$\frac{1}{2}$	$\frac{3}{2}$, $\frac{1}{2}$	1 , 0	$-\frac{1}{2}$, $\frac{1}{2}$
$-\frac{1}{2}$	$\frac{3}{2}$, $\frac{1}{2}$	0 , -1	$-\frac{1}{2}$, $\frac{1}{2}$
$-\frac{3}{2}$	$\frac{3}{2}$	-1	$-\frac{1}{2}$

It is immediately clear that for $m = \frac{3}{2}$ there is only one possibility

$$|\tfrac{3}{2}, \tfrac{3}{2}\rangle = |1, 1\rangle|\tfrac{1}{2}, \tfrac{1}{2}\rangle, \qquad (4.37)$$

$$\therefore \quad C(1, \tfrac{1}{2}, \tfrac{3}{2}; 1, \tfrac{1}{2}, \tfrac{3}{2}) = 1. \qquad (4.38)$$

Now let us operate on eqn (4.37) with the stepping operator, J_-. Using eqn (4.29) and the Condon and Shortley phase convention and remembering that hermitian operators obey eqn (1.2a), we obtain

$$|\tfrac{3}{2}, \tfrac{1}{2}\rangle = \sqrt{\tfrac{1}{3}}|1, 1\rangle|\tfrac{1}{2}, -\tfrac{1}{2}\rangle + \sqrt{\tfrac{2}{3}}|1, 0\rangle|\tfrac{1}{2}, \tfrac{1}{2}\rangle, \qquad (4.39a)$$

$$|\tfrac{3}{2}, -\tfrac{1}{2}\rangle = \sqrt{\tfrac{2}{3}}|1, 0\rangle|\tfrac{1}{2}, -\tfrac{1}{2}\rangle + \sqrt{\tfrac{1}{3}}|1, -1\rangle|\tfrac{1}{2}, \tfrac{1}{2}\rangle, \qquad (4.39b)$$

$$|\tfrac{3}{2}, -\tfrac{3}{2}\rangle = |1, -1\rangle|\tfrac{1}{2}, -\tfrac{1}{2}\rangle. \qquad (4.39c)$$

Next, consider the states for which $j = \frac{1}{2}$. Let us write

$$|\tfrac{1}{2}, \tfrac{1}{2}\rangle = a|1, 1\rangle|\tfrac{1}{2}, -\tfrac{1}{2}\rangle + b|1, 0\rangle|\tfrac{1}{2}, \tfrac{1}{2}\rangle. \qquad (4.40)$$

Now it is clear from the table of allowed quantum numbers that

$|\frac{3}{2}, \frac{1}{2}\rangle, |\frac{1}{2}, \frac{1}{2}\rangle$ are the *only* states of total angular momentum which decompose into the states given by the right hand sides of eqns (4.39a), (4.40). Since conversion between the two sets of basis states must take place by a *unitary* transformation (cf. eqn (1.65)), it follows that the matrix

$$M = \begin{pmatrix} \sqrt{\frac{1}{3}} & \sqrt{\frac{2}{3}} \\ a & b \end{pmatrix} \qquad (4.41)$$

must be unitary. Hence it is easy to see that

$$a = \sqrt{(\tfrac{2}{3})}\, e^{i\alpha}, \qquad b = -\sqrt{(\tfrac{1}{3})}\, e^{i\alpha}. \qquad (4.42)$$

where α is real but undetermined. It is usually set to zero *by convention*. This is the second part of the Condon and Shortley phase convention. The first part relates the phases of states with the same value of j but different values of m. The second relates the phases of states with the same values of m but different values of j.

$$\therefore \quad |\tfrac{1}{2}, \tfrac{1}{2}\rangle = \sqrt{\tfrac{2}{3}}|1, 1\rangle|\tfrac{1}{2}, -\tfrac{1}{2}\rangle - \sqrt{\tfrac{1}{3}}|1, 0\rangle|\tfrac{1}{2}, \tfrac{1}{2}\rangle. \qquad (4.43)$$

Finally, using eqn (4.29) again,

$$|\tfrac{1}{2}, -\tfrac{1}{2}\rangle = \sqrt{\tfrac{1}{3}}|1, 0\rangle|\tfrac{1}{2}, -\tfrac{1}{2}\rangle - \sqrt{\tfrac{2}{3}}|1, -1\rangle|\tfrac{1}{2}, \tfrac{1}{2}\rangle. \qquad (4.44)$$

This gives a complete set of Clebsch–Gordan coefficients for $j_1 = 1$, $j_2 = \frac{1}{2}$. The coefficients for any other pair of angular momenta can be calculated by exactly the same method. In most practical calculations, of course, they are looked up in tables or generated by standard computer programmes.

So far, the discussion has been completely general. It does not assume any specific algebra for the state functions or operators. However, the philosophy of Chapter 1 immediately suggests a form provided that j is fixed. In this form, ϕ is represented by a $(2j+1)$-dimensional vector with components a_m, say, where m is the quantum number corresponding to J_z. The angular momentum operators are represented by $(2j+1) \times (2j+1)$ matrices. J_z is a diagonal matrix with elements running from j to $-j$ (cf. eqn (4.15)). J_+, J_- are matrices with non-zero elements only between states for which the quantum number, m, differs by unity (cf. eqns (4.28), (4.29)). It follows from eqns (4.18) that

$$J_x = \tfrac{1}{2}(J_+ + J_-), \qquad J_y = \tfrac{1}{2}(1/i)(J_+ - J_-). \qquad (4.45)$$

Since the matrix elements of J_+, J_- are chosen to be real by the Condon and Shortley phase convention, J_x is real and J_y is imaginary.

The implications of the convention are most easily seen by using eqns (4.28), (4.29) to construct two rather more general angular momentum operators J'_x, J'_y for which the phase restriction does not hold.

$$J'_x = \tfrac{1}{2}(e^{i\alpha} J_+ + e^{-i\alpha} J_-) \quad = J_x \cos\alpha - J_y \sin\alpha,$$
$$J'_y = \tfrac{1}{2}(1/i)(e^{i\alpha} J_+ - e^{-i\alpha} J_-) = J_x \sin\alpha + J_y \cos\alpha. \qquad (4.46)$$

It follows from elementary geometry that J'_x, J'_y are obtained from J_x, J_y *by rotation by an angle α about the z axis.* Thus the Condon and Shortley phase convention implies a *choice of x, y axes.* Clearly, any other choice would also satisfy the commutation relations (4.14). This fact will be important when we come to consider the phase conventions used in G-parity.

Using eqns (4.15), (4.28), (4.29), (4.45) and the Condon and Shortley phase convention, it is easy to see that the expectation values of the three components of angular momentum are given by

$$\langle J_x \rangle = \sum_{m=-j}^{j-1} \mathrm{Re}(a^*_{m+1} a_m)[j(j+1) - m(m+1)]^{\frac{1}{2}}\hbar,$$
$$\langle J_y \rangle = \sum_{m=-j}^{j-1} \mathrm{Im}(a^*_{m+1} a_m)[j(j+1) - m(m+1)]^{\frac{1}{2}}\hbar,$$
$$\langle J_z \rangle = \sum_{m=-j}^{j} m|a_m|^2\hbar, \qquad (4.47)$$

where Re and Im denote real and imaginary parts respectively. The polarization vector then follows from eqn (4.32).

It may be helpful to illustrate the matrix and vector representation of angular momentum states by some examples. Suppose that $j = \tfrac{1}{2}$. Then

$$J_x = \tfrac{1}{2}\begin{pmatrix} 0 & 1 \\ 1 & 0 \end{pmatrix}\hbar, J_y = \tfrac{1}{2}\begin{pmatrix} 0 & -i \\ i & 0 \end{pmatrix}\hbar, J_z = \tfrac{1}{2}\begin{pmatrix} 1 & 0 \\ 0 & -1 \end{pmatrix}\hbar. \qquad (4.48)$$

These matrices are the familiar Pauli spin matrices. Any state with $j = \tfrac{1}{2}$ can be represented by a vector with components $a_{\frac{1}{2}}, a_{-\frac{1}{2}}$ where

$$|a_{\frac{1}{2}}|^2 + |a_{-\frac{1}{2}}|^2 = 1, \qquad (4.49)$$

by normalization. In particular, the angular momentum eigenstates are represented by the vectors

$$\begin{pmatrix} 1 \\ 0 \end{pmatrix}, \quad j = \tfrac{1}{2}, \quad m = \tfrac{1}{2},$$

$$\begin{pmatrix} 0 \\ 1 \end{pmatrix}, \quad j = \tfrac{1}{2}, \quad m = -\tfrac{1}{2}. \qquad (4.50)$$

The angular momentum expectation values along the x, y, z axes can be derived using eqns (4.47):

$$\langle J_x \rangle = \text{Re } a^*_{\frac{1}{2}} a_{-\frac{1}{2}}, \qquad \langle J_y \rangle = \text{Im } a^*_{\frac{1}{2}} a_{-\frac{1}{2}},$$

$$\langle J_z \rangle = \tfrac{1}{2}(a^*_{\frac{1}{2}} a_{\frac{1}{2}} - a^*_{-\frac{1}{2}} a_{-\frac{1}{2}}). \tag{4.51}$$

It is easy to see that all states with $j = \frac{1}{2}$ are fully polarized and thus that any one of them may be obtained from the eigenstates (4.50) by a suitable spatial rotation. Similarly, if $j = 1$ then

$$J_x = \sqrt{\tfrac{1}{2}} \begin{pmatrix} 0 & 1 & 0 \\ 1 & 0 & 1 \\ 0 & 1 & 0 \end{pmatrix} \hbar, \qquad J_y = \sqrt{\tfrac{1}{2}} \begin{pmatrix} 0 & -i & 0 \\ i & 0 & -i \\ 0 & i & 0 \end{pmatrix} \hbar,$$

$$J_z = \begin{pmatrix} 1 & 0 & 0 \\ 0 & 0 & 0 \\ 0 & 0 & -1 \end{pmatrix} \hbar, \tag{4.52}$$

and any state with $j = 1$ can be represented by a vector with components a_1, a_0, a_{-1} where

$$|a_1|^2 + |a_0|^2 + |a_{-1}|^2 = 1 \tag{4.53}$$

by normalization. The angular momentum expectation values along the x, y, z axes are

$$\langle J_x \rangle = \sqrt{2} \, \text{Re}(a^*_1 a_0 + a^*_0 a_{-1})$$

$$\langle J_y \rangle = \sqrt{2} \, \text{Im}(a^*_1 a_0 + a^*_0 a_{-1})$$

$$\langle J_z \rangle = a^*_1 a_1 - a^*_{-1} a_{-1}. \tag{4.54}$$

However, by no means all states with $j = 1$ are fully polarized. Many of them cannot be obtained from the eigenstates by suitable spatial rotations.

This matrix and vector representation of angular momentum algebra has been derived using as its *only* physical assumptions the commutation relations (4.14) and the fact that state functions can be normalized. In fact, it can be shown that, for any symmetry operation *all* matrix and vector representations can be found by discovering all sets of generators which satisfy the required commutation relations for the operation. The present method for constructing generators is useful in a great many cases, but it is not unique. And it has certain serious disadvantages. Its treatment of different angular momentum states is not uniform—the specific form of the generators, J_x, J_y, J_z

depends on the quantum number, j. One could, of course, write all angular momentum states of whatever j, m as vectors provided that the vectors are sufficiently large. It would then be possible to use a single set of generators, but the disadvantages of such unwieldly notation should hardly need stressing. Also, the operators, J_x, J_y, J_z, can generate some but not all of the possible unitary transformations. We saw, for instance, that some angular momentum vectors have $j = 1$ but $|\mathbf{P}| < 1$. These cannot be formed by rotating the angular momentum eigenstates with $a_1 = 1$ or $a_{-1} = 1$. Finally, it is difficult to devise a vector formalism to describe the addition of two angular momenta. It can be done, but the notation is extremely cumbersome. In short, the notation is both too cumbersome and too general to be entirely suitable. We must therefore look for an alternative and more economical way to write our operators and state functions. This in turn requires a discussion of special unitary transformations and tensor algebra.

4.3. Angular momentum and SU_2

The next two sections examine an alternative representation for some of the consequences of the commutation relations (4.14). This representation is based on the tensor algebra of SU_2 and the greater part of the discussion is purely algebraic. It must be emphasized that no new physics is being introduced at this point. Only the notation is being changed. However, the new notation has a number of advantages. It is more compact. The same set of generators is used for all rotations and every unitary transformation can be interpreted as producing a definite rotation. Simple rules give the necessary and sufficient conditions which a tensor must satisfy if it is to describe an angular momentum eigenstate or a state formed by rotation of an angular momentum eigenstate. Moreover, the formalism describing the addition of angular momenta emerges in a natural way. Finally, the notation makes it easy to relate the properties of angular momentum to those of other symmetries. The essential physics of isospin can be displayed in a particularly natural way; G-parity and time reversal are easily described and the extension to SU_3 follows by a development of the algebra with no further conceptual problems. The present section introduces the special unitary transformations and explains why they are important. It then goes on to show that SU_2 is the appropriate symmetry for describing angular momentum. First, the generators of SU_2 satisfy commutation relations of the form (4.14). Secondly, every transformation in SU_2 corresponds to a unique three dimensional rotation and every rotation corresponds to a pair of SU_2 transformations. The correspondence is thus one to two. For our present purposes, the ambiguity is unimportant. The two SU_2 transformations are identical except for sign. The next section develops the essential tensor algebra.

SU_2, SU_3 and SU_6 are sets of special unitary transformations, that is, transformations produced by square matrices which are *unitary* and which have determinants equal to 1 (and hence are *special*). The numbers 2, 3, 6 give the numbers of rows and columns in the matrices. First, let us consider why such transformations are so important in physics. We showed in Chapter 1 that all symmetry operators which do not involve time reversal are unitary. It remains to understand the implications of the word 'special'. Now

$$(\text{modulus } |T|)^2 = |T^*| \, |T| = |T^\dagger T| = |I| = 1, \qquad (4.55)$$

where we have used eqns (1.41), (1.54). Hence

$$|T| = e^{i\alpha}. \qquad (4.56)$$

where α is a real number. Thus the *special* requirement is equivalent to *defining the phase*, α, of the determinant of the transforming matrix to be zero. This definition can be made without loss of generality since, as we have emphasized repeatedly, the absolute phase of any state function is undetermined. Consequently the phase of any unitary symmetry operator can be chosen arbitrarily. It follows that the most general unitary symmetry transformation is physically equivalent to the special unitary transformation.

Special unitary transformations are continuous and can therefore be described in terms of their generators. We have already seen that these must be hermitian, but the requirement that the phase angle, α, be zero has an important further implication. Remember that, by eqn (4.4), any infinitesimal transformation can be written

$$T(\delta) = I + i\delta \sum_j a_j R_j, \qquad (4.57)$$

where the R_j are generators, the a_j are expansion coefficients and δ is infinitesimal. Clearly, the matrix $T(\delta)$ has finite diagonal elements and infinitesimal off-diagonal elements. Let us evaluate the determinant of $T(\delta)$ ignoring terms of order δ^2. This means that we need include only the diagonal elements since, by the definition (1.37) of a determinant, if we include one off-diagonal element in any term, we must include at least two. For instance, suppose that $\sum_j a_j R_j$ is given by the 2×2

matrix

$$\sum_j a_j R_j = \begin{pmatrix} r_1^1 & r_1^2 \\ r_2^1 & r_2^2 \end{pmatrix}, \tag{4.58}$$

then

$$|T(\delta)| = (1 + i\delta r_1^1)(1 + i\delta r_2^2) + \delta^2 r_1^2 r_2^1. \tag{4.59}$$

The last term is of second order in δ and can therefore be neglected. But the product of the diagonal elements in $T(\delta)$ is given to first order in δ by

$$|T(\delta)| = 1 + i\delta \operatorname{Tr}\left(\sum_j a_j R_j\right), \tag{4.60}$$

where Tr indicates the trace of a matrix, that is the *sum* of its diagonal elements. If $|T(\delta)|$ is equal to unity then

$$\operatorname{Tr}\left(\sum_j a_j R_j\right) = 0. \tag{4.61}$$

But, since this is true for all choices of a_j, it follows that the trace of every generator must be zero. The generators of special unitary transformations are *hermitian* and *traceless*.

Now consider the *number* of generators needed for each group of transformations. By construction, this is equal to the number needed for all possible infinitesimal transformations. Now, since all infinitesimal transformations can be expressed in the form (4.57), it is clear that the number of generators of SU_n is equal to the number of linearly independent, hermitian, traceless, $n \times n$ matrices. Each such matrix depends on $n^2 - 1$ independent parameters and it follows that there must be $n^2 - 1$ linearly independent generators. Thus SU_2, for instance, will have three generators and this immediately suggests that it might be a suitable symmetry for describing rotations. However, a necessary condition for this is that the generators should satisfy the commutation relations (4.14). It is easy to show that they do. Consider an arbitrary 2×2 hermitian traceless matrix. It depends on three independent parameters and it is convenient to consider them as the real components, r_x, r_y, r_z say, of a three dimensional vector $\mathbf{r}$. Thus the matrix can be written

$$R(\mathbf{r}) = \begin{pmatrix} r_z & r_x - ir_y \\ r_x + ir_y & -r_z \end{pmatrix} \tag{4.62}$$

and there will be a one to one correspondence between vectors, $\mathbf{r}$, and hermitian, traceless matrices, R. This is not, of course, the only possible way in which the three parameters could be introduced, but it is the most convenient for our purpose. A trio of generators could be written $R(\mathbf{a})$, $R(\mathbf{b})$, $R(\mathbf{c})$ and the condition that they should be linearly independent is the same as the condition that $\mathbf{a}$, $\mathbf{b}$, $\mathbf{c}$ should be linearly independent. That is, $\mathbf{a}$, $\mathbf{b}$, $\mathbf{c}$ must be mutually orthogonal.

$$\mathbf{a} \times \mathbf{b} = \alpha \mathbf{c}, \text{ etc.} \tag{4.63}$$

where α is a real constant which can be chosen arbitrarily. Now it can easily be shown using the rule, (1.39), for matrix multiplication that

$$R(\mathbf{a})R(\mathbf{b}) = \mathbf{a} \cdot \mathbf{b}I + iR(\mathbf{a} \times \mathbf{b}) = \mathbf{a} \cdot \mathbf{b}I + i\alpha R(\mathbf{c}). \tag{4.64}$$

Hence, choosing α to be $\tfrac{1}{2}\hbar$, we have

$$[R(\mathbf{a}), R(\mathbf{b})] = i\hbar R(\mathbf{c}). \tag{4.65}$$

Thus the generators of SU_2 satisfy the commutation relations (4.14) for angular momentum. But, since the whole physical content of angular momentum theory was derived from the commutation relations between the generators, it follows that the algebra of SU_2 is the algebra of angular momentum theory. (Note that, since such higher symmetries as SU_3 have more than three generators, spatial rotations can at most form a subset of these symmetries.)

One further problem remains to be solved. Any finite rotation can be described in terms of the Euler angles, α, β, γ (cf. eqn (4.31)). These have a straightforward geometrical interpretation. However, SU_2 transformations depend on different parameters and their meaning is much less obvious. We have seen that their generators satisfy the correct commutation relations, but we have not yet given them a geometrical interpretation. Nor have we said anything about the range that is covered. It is therefore necessary to show that each SU_2 transformation can be represented by a three dimensional rotation and conversely that each three dimensional rotation can be represented by an SU_2 transformation. In order to do this, we must set up explicit relations between them.

First consider the choice of coordinate systems. We have seen that the essential physics of spatial rotations can be derived from the commutation relations (4.14), but that axes can be chosen arbitrarily. In the last section, eqn (4.15) defined the z-axis and the Condon and Shortley phase convention defined the x- and y-axes. For SU_2, a convenient choice of the orthogonal vectors, **a**, **b**, **c**, is

$$\mathbf{a} = \tfrac{1}{2}\hbar \begin{pmatrix} 1 \\ 0 \\ 0 \end{pmatrix}, \qquad \mathbf{b} = \tfrac{1}{2}\hbar \begin{pmatrix} 0 \\ 1 \\ 0 \end{pmatrix}, \qquad \mathbf{c} = \tfrac{1}{2}\hbar \begin{pmatrix} 0 \\ 0 \\ 1 \end{pmatrix}. \tag{4.66}$$

Note that, since the normalization constant, α, was chosen to make eqns (4.65) identical with (4.14), the only remaining freedom corresponds to a choice of axes. Thus the definition (4.66) does not introduce any new physics. Using eqn (4.62), it is clear that the generators become

$$R(\mathbf{a}) = \tfrac{1}{2}\hbar \begin{pmatrix} 0 & 1 \\ 1 & 0 \end{pmatrix}, \qquad R(\mathbf{b}) = \tfrac{1}{2}\hbar \begin{pmatrix} 0 & -i \\ i & 0 \end{pmatrix}, \qquad R(\mathbf{c}) = \tfrac{1}{2}\hbar \begin{pmatrix} 1 & 0 \\ 0 & -1 \end{pmatrix},$$
$$\tag{4.67}$$

and that these are identical with J_x, J_y, J_z (eqn (4.48)). Thus the choice of axes, (4.66), is exactly the same as that used in the last section.

Now let us interpret the generators (4.67) physically. Eqn (4.62) sets up a one-to-one correspondence between vectors, **r**, and hermitian traceless matrices, R. Consider the behaviour of R under an infinitesimal SU_2 transformation:

$$T(\delta) = I + i\delta R(\mathbf{a})/\hbar. \tag{4.68}$$

Comparison with eqns (4.7), (4.11), (4.66) shows that this must in some sense correspond to a rotation by $-\delta$ about the x-axis.

$$\begin{aligned}
R(\mathbf{r}') &= T(\delta)R(\mathbf{r})T(\delta)^{-1} \\
&= \left(I + \frac{i\delta R(\mathbf{a})}{\hbar}\right)R(r)\left(I - \frac{i\delta R(\mathbf{a})}{\hbar}\right) \\
&= R(\mathbf{r}) + \frac{i\delta}{\hbar}[R(\mathbf{a}), R(\mathbf{r})] = R(\mathbf{r}) + \frac{2\delta}{\hbar}R(\mathbf{r} \times \mathbf{a}),
\end{aligned} \tag{4.69}$$

where we have used eqn (4.64).

$$\therefore \quad \mathbf{r}' = \mathbf{r} + \frac{2\delta}{\hbar}\mathbf{r} \times \mathbf{a}, \tag{4.70}$$

so that

$$r'_x = r_x, \qquad r'_y = r_y + \delta r_z, \qquad r'_z = r_z - \delta r_y.$$

But this is just the expression for a rotation of **r** by $-\delta$ about the x-axis! It is easy to see that similar results can be derived for rotations about the y- and z-axes. Thus, using the convention (4.66), SU_2 transformations have an extremely simple geometrical interpretation.

If three dimensional vectors, **r**, are represented by 2×2 hermitian traceless matrices, R, then three dimensional rotations can be represented by SU_2 transformations.

It remains, however, to show that the ranges are the same. That is, that every SU_2 transformation can be represented by a three dimensional rotation and vice versa. The first part of this statement is easily proved. Consider an arbitrary hermitian, traceless matrix, $R(\mathbf{r})$, corresponding to a vector, **r**. Under an SU_2 similarity transformation by an operator, T, it will be changed to a new matrix, R', which is also hermitian and traceless (cf. Sections 1.2, 1.3) but which corresponds to a new three dimensional vector, **r**′.

$$R'(\mathbf{r}) = TR(\mathbf{r})T^{-1} = R(\mathbf{r}'). \qquad (4.71)$$

Now

$$|R(\mathbf{r})| = -r_z{}^2 - (r_x - \mathrm{i}r_y)(r_x + \mathrm{i}r_y) = -\mathbf{r} \cdot \mathbf{r}. \qquad (4.72)$$

But the determinant of any matrix is left unchanged by a similarity transformation (cf. discussion of eqn (1.74)).

$$\therefore \quad \mathbf{r} \cdot \mathbf{r} = \mathbf{r}' \cdot \mathbf{r}'. \qquad (4.73)$$

Now the condition that the square, $\mathbf{r} \cdot \mathbf{r}$, of the magnitude of any vector, **r**, should be left unchanged is *precisely* the condition for a three dimensional rotation. Hence *every* SU_2 transformation corresponds to a three dimensional rotation.

Finally, we must show that every rotation can be represented by an SU_2 transformation. Rotations are most easily expressed in terms of the Euler angles α, β, γ and the most general rotation is given by eqn (4.31). Consider first a rotation by an angle, γ, about the z-axis. The corresponding SU_2 transformation is given by

$$T(0, 0, \gamma) = \exp[-\mathrm{i}\gamma R(\mathbf{c})/\hbar] = I - \mathrm{i}\gamma R(\mathbf{c})/\hbar + (\mathrm{i}\gamma R(\mathbf{c})/\hbar)^2/2! - \ldots$$

$$= \begin{pmatrix} 1 & 0 \\ 0 & 1 \end{pmatrix} \cos \tfrac{1}{2}\gamma - \mathrm{i} \begin{pmatrix} 1 & 0 \\ 0 & -1 \end{pmatrix} \sin \tfrac{1}{2}\gamma$$

$$= \begin{pmatrix} \mathrm{e}^{-\frac{1}{2}\mathrm{i}\gamma} & 0 \\ 0 & \mathrm{e}^{\frac{1}{2}\mathrm{i}\gamma} \end{pmatrix}, \qquad (4.74)$$

where we have used the facts that $\cos x$, $\sin x$ are respectively even and odd functions of x and that

$$R(\mathbf{c})R(\mathbf{c}) = \tfrac{1}{4}\hbar^2 I. \qquad (4.75)$$

By exactly analogous reasoning

$$T(0, \beta, 0) = \begin{pmatrix} \cos \frac{1}{2}\beta & -\sin \frac{1}{2}\beta \\ \sin \frac{1}{2}\beta & \cos \frac{1}{2}\beta \end{pmatrix}. \tag{4.76}$$

$$\therefore \quad T(\alpha, \beta, \gamma) = \begin{pmatrix} \exp\{-\frac{1}{2}i(\alpha+\gamma)\} \cos \frac{1}{2}\beta & -\exp\{-\frac{1}{2}i(\alpha-\gamma)\} \sin \frac{1}{2}\beta \\ \exp\{\frac{1}{2}i(\alpha-\gamma)\} \sin \frac{1}{2}\beta & \exp\{\frac{1}{2}i(\alpha+\gamma)\} \cos \frac{1}{2}\beta \end{pmatrix}.$$

$$\tag{4.77}$$

This is a special unitary matrix. It follows that any rotation can be represented by an SU_2 transformation. Note that the geometrical effect of a rotation is not altered if 2π is added to α, β or γ. However, this would change the sign of T. It follows that a given rotation specifies T only up to a factor of ± 1 and that the correspondence between rotations and SU_2 transformations is one to two. However, for our present purposes the ambiguity is unimportant. This completes the proof that SU_2 is an appropriate set of symmetry transformations for describing angular momentum. We have also seen how to construct the various SU_2 operators. But in order to describe the SU_2 state functions, it is necessary to introduce some tensor algebra.

4.4. Some tensor algebra

This section sets up the angular momentum state functions in SU_2 formalism, interprets them physically, and considers how they transform under spatial rotations. In order to do this, it is necessary to replace the state vectors of Section 4.2 with state *tensors*, and to define two types of operation on these tensors. Operations of the first type are symmetry transformations using the special unitary matrices which were introduced in the last section. These transformations are analogous to the transformations (1.61) of state vectors introduced in Chapter 1. Since, as we have seen, all possible special unitary matrices represent real three dimensional rotations, every SU_2 transformation has an immediate physical interpretation. Operations of the second type correspond to physical measurements. In the present context, such measurements are determinations of angular momentum quantum numbers or expectation values. These operations are analogous to the operations, RV, $V^\dagger RV$, performed on state vectors (cf. eqns (1.68), (1.83)). Because of the somewhat more complex structure of state tensors, hermitian operations corresponding to measurements do not have the same form as unitary operations corresponding to symmetry transformations. However, the relationship between the two can be derived using eqn (4.2). Another important concept is that of *reduction* of a tensor. The formalism makes it possible to write down tensors corresponding to mixed states which are not eigenstates of total angular momentum. It is important to be able to divide these up into states of pure total angular momentum. This process is called reduction. The final part of this section describes how reduction is carried out and gives the rules for recognizing those states which cannot be reduced further. These rules are independent of the choice of co-ordinate axes.

First, let us introduce the idea of a tensor. In the familiar notation of Section 1.2, an element of a covariant vector, V, is written as V_j, where j can take any value from 1 to n and n is the dimension of the space. For SU_2, of course, $n = 2$. Similarly, an element of a matrix, A, is written as A_p^j, where now both j and p can run from 1 to n. A tensor is a simple generalization of these ideas. An element of a tensor, A, is written

$$A_{pq...t}^{jk...m} \qquad (4.78)$$

where every index can run from 1 to n. In general, a tensor has several *covariant* (lower) indices and several *contravariant* (upper) indices. The total number of indices is called the *rank* of the tensor. Thus, a vector is a tensor of the first rank, a matrix is a tensor of the second rank, and so on. The importance of tensors in SU_2 theory is that they represent the parts of state functions which describe angular momentum.

We next introduce the two types of operation which can be applied to tensors. First, consider any special unitary matrix, T. The transformation of a tensor, A, under T follows from a simple extension of eqns (1.40), (1.62) and (1.133). It is written as

$$A' = TA. \qquad (4.79)$$

Eqn (4.79) gives the conventional notation for the transformation of A to a new tensor, A', with elements

$$A_{pq...t}^{'jk...m} = T_p^\alpha T_q^\beta \ldots T_t^\gamma A_{\alpha\beta...\gamma}^{\lambda\mu...\pi}(T^\dagger)_\lambda (T^\dagger)_\mu^k \ldots (T^\dagger)_\pi^m, \qquad (4.80)$$

where we use the customary summation convention. Eqn (4.80) should be considered as part of the *definition* of a tensor. It is easy to see, however, that it reduces to familiar forms when applied to vectors and matrices

$$A'_p = T_p^\alpha A_\alpha, \qquad A'^j = A^\lambda (T^\dagger)_\lambda^j, \qquad A'_p^j = T_p^\alpha A_\alpha^\lambda (T^\dagger)_\lambda^j, \qquad (4.81)$$

cf. eqns (1.40), (1.62) and (1.133).

Secondly, consider the hermitian operations corresponding to measurements. The transformation of a tensor, A, under an hermitian operator, R, is easily derived by remembering that R can be considered as the generator of a unitary operator, T. Consider the infinitesimal transformation $T(\delta)$. Using eqn (4.2) and neglecting terms of order δ^2, we find

$$A' = T(\delta)A = (I + i\delta R)A, \qquad (4.82)$$

and this has elements

$$A'^{jk...m}_{pq...t} = A^{jk...m}_{pq...t} + i\delta\{R^{\alpha}_p A^{jk...m}_{\alpha q...t} + \ldots + R^{\gamma}_t A^{jk...m}_{pq...\gamma} - A^{\lambda k...m}_{pq...t} R^{j}_{\lambda} - \ldots - A^{jk...\nu}_{pq...t} R^{m}_{\nu}\}; \qquad (4.83)$$

where we have used the fact that R is hermitian. A suitable shorthand notation for eqn (4.83) is

$$A' = A + i\delta[RA] \qquad (4.84)$$

where $[RA]$ is a new tensor. An element of $[RA]$ is given by

$$[RA]^{jk...m}_{pq...t} = R^{\alpha}_p A^{jk...m}_{\alpha q...t} + \ldots + R^{\gamma}_t A^{jk...m}_{pq,...\gamma} - A^{\lambda k...m}_{pq...t} R^{j}_{\lambda} - \ldots - A^{jk...\nu}_{pq...t} R^{m}_{\nu}. \qquad (4.85)$$

This provides a convenient general definition of the transformation of A under an hermitian operator, R. If A is an eigenstate of R, then it will satisfy the usual eigenvalue equation

$$[RA] = rA, \qquad (4.86)$$

(cf. eqn (1.1)). Again, it is easy to see that, for the simple case in which A is a vector, eqn (4.86) reduces to the familiar form

$$[RA]_p = R^{\alpha}_p A_{\alpha} = rA_p. \qquad (4.87)$$

To sum up: we have distinguished two types of operation on tensors—special unitary transformations, which occur in symmetry principles, and which are defined by eqn (4.80), and hermitian operations, which occur in the corresponding conservation laws, and which are defined by eqn (4.85).

This completes the discussion of the SU_2 behaviour of tensors. If they are used to represent angular momentum state functions, then we know how to determine their properties, and we know how they transform under spatial rotations. However, we have not yet shown that every angular momentum state function *can* be represented by a tensor. Indeed, the argument is a good deal less simple than the corresponding argument for the matrix and vector formalism. In Section 4.2, we showed that any state of angular momentum, j, can be expressed in terms of $2j + 1$ linearly independent basis states. These basis states can be labelled conveniently by the quantum number, m. Under an arbitrary spatial rotation or stepping operation, the state changes to a new linear combination of the basis states. However, the total number of basis states is unchanged. This is entirely reasonable since such operations leave the total angular momentum, j, unchanged. It was therefore convenient to represent angular momentum state functions by $2j + 1$ dimensional vectors. Any state of integral or half integral j could be represented in this way.

At first sight, replacing state vectors by state tensors introduces no problem. Both the special unitary transformations, (4.80), and the hermitian transformations, (4.85), transform any tensor into a linear combination of tensor elements of the same rank. It would seem that these tensor elements form a basis just as do the elements of a state vector in the more familiar formulation of quantum mechanics. However, at this point a difficulty arises. The number of elements in a tensor of dimension n and rank r is n^r and, for a given dimension, this number can take only a very limited set of values. For SU_2, it can take 1, 2, 4, 8, etc. but not 3 or 5. How then are we to represent states of angular momentum 1 or 2? For the former, we require three linearly independent tensor elements. For the latter, we require five. In neither case is it sufficient to restrict ourselves to tensor elements of a given rank. We must choose suitable *linear combinations* of tensor elements to form basis states.

In particular, if any state is expressed as a linear combination of basis tensors, then it must transform under rotations to another linear combination of the same basis tensors. Thus the first requirement for a suitable set of basis tensors is that any special unitary transformation, T, should convert any member of the set into a linear combination of other members of the set. Since T leaves the rank unchanged, sets of basis tensors must all have the same rank and must therefore all be linear combinations of elements of a given tensor. They must be derived by dividing tensors of a given rank into self contained sets such that the members of each set transform only amongst themselves. This subdivision is known as *reduction* and a tensor which cannot be reduced is said to be *irreducible*. In what follows, we first consider how reduction is carried out and then show that the elements of an irreducible tensor form a suitable set of angular momentum basis states.

In any discussion of reduction, we must understand the behaviour of tensors under SU_2 transformations. Particular interest attaches to combinations of tensors which are invariant under such transformations. These combinations are analogous to scalar products in vector algebra or Lorentz invariants in special relativity. Now, in a purely formal way, it is easy to form scalars as the *inner products* of two tensors provided that each has as many lower indices as the other has upper indices

$$S = A^{jk...m}_{pq...t} B^{pq...t}_{jk...m}.$$

(4.88)

We follow the summation convention as usual. A familiar special case is the scalar product of two vectors

$$S = A^j B_j.$$

(4.89)

Eqns (4.80), (4.88) imply that

$$S' \equiv TS = S.$$

(4.90)

The general proof of this is elementary, but the large number of indices make it rather cumbersome. We content ourselves with proving it for the special case, (4.89).

$$S' = A^\lambda (T^\dagger)^j_\lambda T^\alpha_j B_\alpha = A^\lambda (T^\dagger T)^\alpha_\lambda B_\alpha = A^\lambda I^\alpha_\lambda B_\alpha = A^\lambda B_\lambda = S.$$

(4.91)

It is easy to see by analogy that eqn (4.90) is true in general.

Next notice that certain tensors, although they are not scalars, have the property that their elements are left unchanged by any special unitary transformation, T. One of these is the δ tensor (cf. eqn (1.26)).

$$\delta'^j_p = T^\alpha_p \delta^\lambda_\alpha (T^\dagger)^j_\lambda = T^\alpha_p (T^\dagger)^j_\alpha = (TT^\dagger)^j_p = I^j_p = \delta^j_p,$$

(4.92)

where successive steps are achieved by summing over λ, α. Another is the *totally antisymmetric tensor* defined by

$\epsilon_{pq...t} = 1$ for $p, q, \ldots, t = 1, 2, \ldots, n$ or some even permutation of this order

$\quad = -1$ for any odd permutation of this order

$\quad = 0$ if any pair of indices, p and q say, are equal.

If p, q, etc. can take any value from 1 to n, where n is the dimension of the space, then ϵ has n lower indices. ϵ has already been used in the definition, (1.37), of a determinant and this definition forms a convenient starting point for showing that ϵ is left unchanged by any special unitary transformation. The proof takes place in three stages. Let ϵ transform under T to a new tensor ϵ'. Then we first show that $\epsilon'_{12\ldots n}$ is unity

$$|T| = T_1^p T_2^q \ldots T_n^t \epsilon_{pq\ldots t} = (T\epsilon)_{12\ldots n} = \epsilon'_{12\ldots n}. \qquad (4.93)$$

But the determinant of any special unitary matrix is equal to 1 and the result is proved. Secondly, note that if a pair of indices is transposed then the sign of ϵ' is changed. For instance

$$\epsilon'_{21\ldots n} = T_2^p T_1^q \ldots T_n^t \epsilon_{pq\ldots t} = -T_1^q T_2^p \ldots T_n^t \epsilon_{qp\ldots t}$$
$$= -|T| = -1, \qquad (4.94)$$

where the second stage uses the definition of ϵ. Thirdly, it follows from equations of the form (4.94) that if any two indices of ϵ' are equal then that element of ϵ' is zero. Hence ϵ' satisfies the definition of ϵ and we conclude

$$\epsilon'_{pq\ldots t} = \epsilon_{pq\ldots t}. \qquad (4.95)$$

In an exactly similar way, it can be shown that a third tensor with elements $\epsilon^{pq\ldots t}$ defined by

$$\epsilon^{pq\ldots t} \equiv \epsilon_{pq\ldots t}, \qquad (4.96)$$

is left unchanged by any special unitary transformation.

We are now in a position to discuss the reduction of tensors. Remember that the elements of a reduced tensor are themselves sets of linear combinations of tensor elements of a given rank and that under special unitary transformations each member of the set turns into a linear combination of other members of the set. Now suppose that we start with a tensor, A, and define a new tensor, B, with elements

$$B_{q\ldots t}^{k\ldots m} \equiv \delta_j^p A_{pq\ldots t}^{jk\ldots m}. \qquad (4.97)$$

By inspection, each element of B is a linear combination of the elements of A. Moreover, it is easy to see that each element of B transforms under T to a linear combination of the original elements of B.

$$B_{q\ldots t}^{\prime k\ldots m} \equiv (TB)_{q\ldots t}^{k\ldots m} = (T\delta_j^p A_p^j)_{q\ldots t}^{k\ldots m}. \qquad (4.98)$$

Consider the implications of this equation. By comparison with the discussion of eqn (4.88), it follows that neither B nor B' depend on the indices j, p. But we have seen that δ_j^p is *invariant* under T. Hence, as far as j, p are concerned, B and B' are the *same* linear combinations of the elements of A. Thus the elements of B' are linear combinations of the elements of B and the result is proved. Now, since B has a smaller number of indices and thus a lower rank than A, it also has a smaller number of elements. Hence, provided that at least some of the elements of B are non zero, all the conditions for tensor reduction have been fulfilled. B is a *reduced tensor* derived from A. The remaining linearly independent combinations of elements of A form another reduced tensor. It follows that A is irreducible only if

$$\delta^p_j A^{jk\ldots m}_{pq,\ldots t} = 0 \tag{4.99}$$

for *any* upper index, j, and *any* lower index, p. It is usual to describe the left hand side of eqn (4.99) as a *trace* of A. Here the word trace is used in a way which is a rather obvious extension of the definition in the discussion of eqn (4.60). One could, for instance, write this definition as

$$\mathrm{Tr}\, A = \delta^p_j A^j_p. \tag{4.100}$$

Of course, a tensor with several upper and lower indices has several traces. It follows that a necessary condition for A to be irreducible is that *all* of its traces should be zero.

Another necessary condition for irreducibility can be derived using the ϵ tensors. We have remarked that if n is the dimension of the space, then ϵ has n indices. Let us start with a tensor, A, and define a new tensor, B, with elements

$$B^{l\ldots m}_{r\ldots sp\ldots t} \equiv \epsilon_{j\ldots kr\ldots s} A^{j\ldots kl\ldots m}_{pq\ldots t}. \tag{4.101}$$

Once again, the elements of B are linear combinations of the elements of A. Also, under any special unitary transformation, T, each element of B transforms to a linear combination of the original elements of B. This time, however, B does not necessarily have a smaller number of indices than A. For instance, if A is a rank two tensor with elements A^j_p, then it is easy to see that B has dimension n and if $n > 2$ then no reduction has occurred. However, it is also clear that in certain circumstances B does have a smaller number of indices than A. In these circumstances, eqn (4.101) implies a reduction provided that at least some of the elements of B are non-zero. In SU_2, for instance, a reduction may be performed using

$$B^{l\ldots m}_{p\ldots t} \equiv \epsilon_{jk} A^{jkl\ldots m}_{p\ldots t}. \tag{4.102}$$

A is irreducible only if B is identically zero and hence if

$$A^{jkl\ldots m}_{p\ldots t} = A^{kjl\ldots m}_{p\ldots t} \tag{4.103}$$

A must be invariant under the permutation of j, k. The same argument can be applied to other pairs of indices and it follows more generally that A is irreducible only if it is invariant under the permutation of any pair of its upper indices. It is then said to be *totally symmetric* in its upper indices. Similarly, using ϵ^{pq}, it is clear that an irreducible SU_2 tensor must be totally symmetric in its lower indices.

Now consider SU_3. A reduction may be performed using

$$B^{l\cdots m}_{rp\ldots t} \equiv \epsilon_{jkr}A^{jkl\cdots m}_{p\ldots t} \tag{4.104}$$

unless all elements of B are zero. Hence, by exactly the same argument, all irreducible SU_3 tensors must be totally symmetric in both upper and lower indices. Thus, for both SU_2 and SU_3, a necessary condition for irreducibility is that the tensors should be totally symmetric and should have vanishing trace. We shall see later that this condition is also sufficient. This rule is extremely important. The derivation makes it clear that it holds with complete generality and that it is independent of the choice of coordinate axes.

This completes the discussion of reduction. We must finally show that the elements of an irreducible tensor form a suitable set of angular momentum basis states. The discussion can be simplified by using a special property of SU_2. Consider the general SU_2 tensor, A, with elements given by eqn (4.78). It follows from the discussion of eqn (4.101) that A obeys the same transformation law as

$$B^{k\cdots m}_{j'pq\ldots t} \equiv \epsilon_{j'j}A^{jk\cdots m}_{pq\ldots t}. \tag{4.105}$$

However, since each index can take only two values, the value of j' is uniquely determined by the value of j. If $j = 1$, then $j' = 2$ and vice versa. Thus eqn (4.105) is *not* a reduction. It states that each element of A can be put in unique one-to-one correspondence with an element of B. By repeating the step from eqn (4.78) to eqn (4.105), it is obvious that, if A is a tensor of rank r with r' covariant and $r-r'$ contravariant indices, then it is equivalent to another tensor of rank r but with all its indices covariant. There is no need to use upper indices at all and the most general SU_2 tensor element can be written in the form

$$A_{pq\ldots t}. \tag{4.106}$$

Now let us suppose that A is irreducible. Each index can take the value one or two, but since A is totally symmetric the value of each element depends on the *number* of ones and twos among its indices and not on their order. Suppose that there are a ones and b twos, then a tensor element can be written as $A(a, b)$ where $a+b = r$ is the rank of the tensor. Using eqns (4.85), (4.48),

$$[J_z A](a, b) = \tfrac{1}{2}(a-b)\hbar A(a, b). \tag{4.107}$$

Thus all elements of A are eigenstates of J_z. Moreover, each element has a different eigenvalue and if we define

$$j \equiv \tfrac{1}{2}(a+b) = \tfrac{1}{2}r, \tag{4.108}$$

then the eigenvalues of J_z run from $-j$ to j. Since the rank, r, of any tensor is integral, j can take the values 0, $\tfrac{1}{2}$, 1, etc., just as did the j defined in Section 4.2. All that remains to be shown is that j satisfies eqns (4.17), (4.26). Now

$$[J^2 A](a, b) = \tfrac{1}{2}b\hbar[J_x A](a+1, b-1) + \tfrac{1}{2}a\hbar]J_x A](a-1, b+1)$$

$$+ \tfrac{1}{2}ib\hbar[J_y A](a+1, b-1) - \tfrac{1}{2}ia\hbar[J_y A](a-1, b+1)$$

$$+ \tfrac{1}{2}(a-b)\hbar[J_z A](a, b)$$

$$= \tfrac{1}{4}\{2b(a+1) + 2a(b+1) + (a-b)^2\}\hbar^2 A(a, b)$$

$$= j(j+1)\hbar^2 A(a, b), \tag{4.109}$$

where we have used eqns (4.85), (4.48). Thus, all elements of A are eigenstates of J^2 and each has the eigenvalue $j(j+1)$. This completes the proof that the elements of irreducible SU_2 tensors can represent angular momentum basis states. The tensor formalism of SU_2 can be used to express all the physics developed in Section 4.2. We have thus developed a theory of angular momentum which is uniform in its treatment of states with different j and we have introduced a set of operators each of which has a definite physical interpretation. The discussion has, however, been somewhat abstract. We shall illustrate it in the next section by a number of special examples. We shall also show that the formalism makes it easy to add two angular momenta together and perform a reduction on the sum. However, it is first necessary to digress briefly in order to introduce the concept of isospin.

4.5. Isospin

This section introduces the concept of isospin, relates it to angular momentum and dicusses some simple examples. It starts by postulating that the strong interaction is invariant under certain transformations and showing that these transformations satisfy the algebra of SU_2. It therefore introduces isospin as a rather abstract analogue of ordinary angular momentum and then shows how it can be interpreted physically.

At first only single nucleons are considered, but the results are easily generalized to include many-nucleon systems. This generalization uses the concept of the direct product of two tensors and the results which are derived can be applied equally well to both angular momentum and isospin. The final part of the section considers the experimental consequences of isospin and the implications of the Wigner–Eckart theorem for strong interactions.

When developing angular momentum theory, we started from the commutation relations between the generators of spatial rotations. From these we derived the usual algebra of state functions and observables. We then showed that there were certain advantages in representing rotations by SU_2 transformations. This led in turn to a reformulation of angular momentum theory using SU_2. The concept of isospin is introduced in a rather different way. The basic idea comes as a generalization of charge independence in nuclear physics. The postulate of charge independence states that the strong interaction does not distinguish the neutron, n, from the proton, p. The generalization states that it does not distinguish either from *any linear combination* of n and p. Thus, although we usually treat n and p as a pair of basis states when discussing the one-nucleon system in nuclear physics, we are not forced by strong interaction theory to do so. Any linearly independent pair of linear combinations of n and p would do equally well. But we have seen in Section 4.3 that choosing a new pair of basis states in the most general possible way corresponds to the most general SU_2 transformation. Our basic assumption is equivalent to saying that the strong interaction is invariant under these SU_2 transformations. Thus we can introduce a new, abstract *isospin space* and say that the strong interaction is *invariant under rotations* in isospin space. The algebra of isospin is identical with the algebra of angular momentum. At present this is introduced simply as a postulate. Its truth or falsity can be determined by testing the resultant predictions.

We have introduced isospin as a symmetry principle, but the general discussion of Section 4.1 shows that, by considering the generators of the symmetry operation, we can obtain the corresponding conservation laws. The method for doing this should now be obvious. We showed in Section 4.3 that the generators of SU_2 satisfy commutation relations of the form (4.14). But it follows from these commutation relations that there are two corresponding conservation laws, those of J_z and J^2. Thus our basic assumption implies two new conserved quantities, *total isospin* and the *third component of isospin*. It should hardly need emphasizing that the word *spin* is used because the algebra is identical with the algebra of ordinary spin and that nothing further should be read into the term.

It follows from this discussion that total isospin and its third component are exactly conserved in strong interactions but not in electromagnetic or weak interactions. Further, as far as the strong interaction is concerned, the choice of the 'direction' of the third component in isospin space is entirely arbitrary. However, the electromagnetic interaction *does* define a 'direction' in isospin space since it distinguishes between neutron and proton. It is therefore usual to choose neutron and proton as a suitable pair of basis states even though this choice is not forced on us by the properties of the strong interaction alone. Nevertheless, the fact that we are unable to 'turn off' the electromagnetic interaction at will implies that the z-axis in isospin space is fixed and so J_x, J_y do not correspond to observables.

Since SU_2 is the symmetry appropriate for both angular momentum and isospin, we can develop the remainder of the algebra for the two together. We shall not at this stage introduce a separate notation for isospin but shall use the operators J^2, J_z indifferently for either angular momentum or isospin. The introduction of isospin, however, gives a convenient opportunity to illustrate many of the ideas introduced in the last section. Let us write the proton, p, and the neutron, n, in the conventional way as column vectors.

$$\text{p} = V_1 = \begin{pmatrix} 1 \\ 0 \end{pmatrix}, \qquad \text{n} = V_2 = \begin{pmatrix} 0 \\ 1 \end{pmatrix}. \tag{4.110}$$

The SU_2 generators are given by eqns (4.48), (4.67). However, since $\hbar$ is not a suitable unit for isospin, we shall set the normalization constant, α, in eqn (4.63) to $\frac{1}{2}$. The action of the generators on the two basis states is given by

$$J_x V_1 = \tfrac{1}{2} V_2, \qquad J_y V_1 = \tfrac{1}{2} i V_2, \qquad J_z V_1 = \tfrac{1}{2} V_1,$$

$$J_x V_2 = \tfrac{1}{2} V_1, \qquad J_y V_2 = -\tfrac{1}{2} i V_1, \qquad J_z V_2 = -\tfrac{1}{2} V_2. \tag{4.111}$$

V_1, V_2 are, of course, eigenstates of J_z by definition. The stepping operators J_+, J_- are defined by eqn (4.18). Their action on the two basis states is given by

$$J_+ V_1 = 0, \qquad J_- V_1 = V_2,$$

$$J_+ V_2 = V_1, \qquad J_- V_2 = 0. \tag{4.112}$$

Note that we are still using the Condon and Shortley phase convention. Finally, the total angular momentum operator, J^2, is defined by eqn (4.16). Its action on the two basis states is given by

$$J^2 V_1 = \tfrac{3}{4} V_1, \qquad J^2 V_2 = \tfrac{3}{4} V_2. \tag{4.113}$$

Now consider the two-nucleon system $V_j V_k$. Its transformation under SU_2 follows from eqn (1.40):

$$V'_j V'_k = T_j^\alpha T_k^\beta V_\alpha V_\beta. \tag{4.114}$$

But this is manifestly just a special case of the rule (4.80) which states how the indices of a tensor transform under SU_2. It is therefore convenient to write the two-nucleon system as the *direct product*, A_{jk}, of the two vectors V_j, V_k.

$$A_{jk} \equiv V_j V_k. \tag{4.115}$$

A is a tensor of the second rank with two covariant indices. It obeys the general tensor transformation law. Similarly, the action of J_z on A is given by

$$[J_z A]_{jk} = J_{zj}^\alpha A_{\alpha k} + J_{zk}^\beta A_{j\beta}, \tag{4.116}$$

which is a special case of eqn (4.85). More explicitly

$$[J_z A]_{11} = A_{11}, \qquad [J_z A]_{12} = [J_z A]_{21} = 0, \qquad [J_z A]_{22} = -A_{22}. \tag{4.117}$$

Thus the third component of isospin emerges, correctly, as an additive quantum number. In order to derive the action of J^2 on A, we notice

$$[J_x A]_{11} = [J_x A]_{22} = \tfrac{1}{2}(A_{12} + A_{21}),$$
$$[J_x A]_{12} = [J_x A]_{21} = \tfrac{1}{2}(A_{11} + A_{22}). \tag{4.118}$$
$$\therefore \quad [J_x^2 A]_{11} = [J_x^2 A]_{22} = \tfrac{1}{2}([J_x A]_{12} + [J_x A]_{21}) = \tfrac{1}{2}(A_{11} + A_{22}),$$
$$[J_x^2 A]_{12} = [J_x^2 A]_{21} = \tfrac{1}{2}([J_x A]_{11} + [J_x A]_{22}) = \tfrac{1}{2}(A_{12} + A_{21}). \tag{4.119}$$

Similarly

$$[J_y^2 A]_{11} = -[J_y^2 A]_{22} = \tfrac{1}{2}(A_{11} - A_{22}),$$
$$[J_y^2 A]_{12} = [J_y^2 A]_{21} = \tfrac{1}{2}(A_{12} + A_{21}). \tag{4.120}$$

Hence, using the definition, (4.16), of J^2, we obtain

$$[J^2 A]_{11} = 2A_{11}, \qquad [J^2 A]_{12} = [J^2 A]_{21} = A_{12} + A_{21},$$
$$[J^2 A]_{22} = 2A_{22}. \tag{4.121}$$

It follows from eqns (4.117), (4.121) that we can form a triplet of simultaneous eigenstates of J^2, J_z:

$$A_{11}, \qquad \sqrt{\tfrac{1}{2}}(A_{12}+A_{21}), \qquad A_{22}; \tag{4.122}$$

where the factor $\sqrt{\tfrac{1}{2}}$ is introduced as a normalization constant. The eigenvalues of J^2 are 2 and those of J_z are $1, 0, -1$ respectively. Similarly, the linear combination

$$\sqrt{\tfrac{1}{2}}(A_{12}-A_{21}) \tag{4.123}$$

is a simultaneous eigenstate of J^2, J_z with both eigenvalues zero. These results are, of course, special cases of the predictions made at the end of the last section.

We have thus divided the four components of the tensor, A, into a triplet and a singlet and we have identified the members of the two multiplets by their different eigenvalues of J^2. However, the important point is that this process corresponds to the reduction of A. It is easy to see this using the standard reduction algorithms developed in Section 4.4. Using the totally antisymmetric tensor, ϵ^{jk}, we can construct

$$S = \epsilon^{jk} A_{jk} = A_{12} - A_{21}. \tag{4.124}$$

But this is just a special case of the invariant scalar, (4.88). It is left unchanged by all SU_2 transformations and it follows from eqn (4.84) that it vanishes under all generators. It is a simultaneous eigenstate of J^2, J_z with both eigenvalues zero. Equally obviously, with suitable normalization it corresponds to (4.123). After subtracting (4.124) there remain three linearly independent combinations of tensor elements. As we saw in the last section, these must be totally symmetric in their lower indices. They are obviously the states, (4.122), already constructed. To sum up, when the tensor, A, is reduced, it is divided into two multiplets, a singlet and a triplet. The elements of a multiplet are distinguished by having different values of J_z. However, within a multiplet, all elements have the same eigenvalue of J^2.

These results are readily generalized to describe the many-nucleon system. For r nucleons, we can write the state tensor, A, by analogy with eqn (4.115) as the direct product of the r vectors V_j, V_k, ..., V_m

$$A_{jk...m} \equiv V_j V_k \ldots V_m; \tag{4.125}$$

A has r covariant indices. As we have seen, this represents the most general possible SU_2 tensor of rank r. Now A is not as it stands totally symmetric in all its indices. It can therefore be reduced and the algorithm, (4.102), can be used to carry out the reduction. Note that this algorithm always changes the rank by two units at a time. Thus, if r is even, then A is a linear combination of irreducible tensors of even rank, and if r is odd then A is a linear combination of tensors of odd rank. The multiplets (4.122), (4.123) offer a special case of this rule. Thus, the isospin part of the state tensor for a many nucleon system can be expressed as a tensor with as many covariant indices as there are nucleons. If this tensor is expressed as the sum of irreducible tensors, then each irreducible tensor corresponds to an isospin multiplet and its elements satisfy eqns (4.107), (4.109). The number of elements in each multiplet is $2j + 1$.

Notice that, although these SU_2 examples all start from the elementary nucleon doublet (4.110), most of the algebra would be exactly the same even if such a doublet did not exist. Eqn (4.108) restricts j to integral and half integral values. But there is no reason in principle why some other symmetry should not restrict it to integral values only. If this happened, then half the states which we have been discussing, including the nucleon doublet, would disappear, but the *algebra* would still be SU_2. We could in fact have introduced our multiplets in a more abstract way without requiring that they be physically constructed from protons and neutrons. This point is important since, as far as we know, just this sort of situation exists in SU_3.

Let us therefore consider a more general case. Suppose that two states, ϕ, χ say, are both simultaneous eigenstates of J^2, J_z with eigenvalues, $j_\phi, m_\phi, j_\chi, m_\chi$ respectively. We showed in Section 4.2 that if ϕ, χ interact the resulting state is an eigenstate of J_z but not in general of J^2. It can be expressed as a linear combination of eigenstates of J^2 and the expansion coefficients are the Clebsch–Gordan coefficients. We shall not discuss the latter again. The method used to determine them is, of course, independent of the notation. Rather, we shall use the SU_2 notation to show which values of j are included in the expansion. The isospin part of the ϕ, χ state functions can be represented by elements of two irreducible tensors, A, B say, with rank $2j_\phi, 2j_\chi$ respectively. The isospin part of the combined state is an element of the direct product tensor, C, say. This element can be written

$$C_{j\ldots t} \equiv A_{jk\ldots m}B_{pq\ldots t};\qquad(4.126)$$

A, B are both irreducible and therefore totally symmetric. However, C can be reduced since

$$D_{k\ldots mq\ldots t} \equiv \epsilon^{jp}C_{jk\ldots mpq\ldots t} \neq 0,\qquad(4.127)$$

as j, p are drawn from different multiplets. Thus the algorithm, (4.102), can be used to reduce C. Since A, B are totally symmetric, exactly the same result will be achieved if ϵ is applied to any other pair of indices provided, of course, that one is drawn from A and the other from B. This first step in the reduction can be represented as

$$C = C' + D; \tag{4.128}$$

C', D are both linear combinations of the elements of C. C' has rank $2j_\phi + 2j_\chi$. It is totally symmetric and therefore irreducible. It represents a multiplet with isospin

$$j_C = j_\phi + j_\chi. \tag{4.129}$$

D contains the remaining linearly independent linear combinations of the elements of C. It has rank $2(j_\phi + j_\chi - 1)$. In general, it is reducible and so can be separated into an irreducible tensor, D' say, with isospin

$$j_D = j_\phi + j_\chi - 1. \tag{4.130}$$

Note that each step in the reduction uses one index from A and one from B. The process can be continued until the supply of indices from either A or B runs out. The final multiplet has isospin $|j_\phi - j_\chi|$. Thus A, B can combine to form multiplets with isospins ranging from $j_\phi + j_\chi$ to $|j_\phi - j_\chi|$, just as one predicts using the normal vectorial argument. Note that, by construction, C has $(2j_\phi + 1)(2j_\chi + 1)$ elements and that the reduced tensors have

$$\sum_{j=|j_\phi - j_\chi|}^{j_\phi + j_\chi} (2j + 1) = (2j_\phi + 1)(2j_\chi + 1) \tag{4.131}$$

elements between them. Hence the procedure exhausts the elements of C.

Two further points are worth mentioning. First, the algorithm always changes the rank by two units at a time. Thus C decomposes into states of integral isospin or states of half integral isospin *but not both*. Secondly, if A and B have the same rank, then it follows from the antisymmetry of ϵ that C' is symmetric under the exchange of A and B, D' is antisymmetric and so on.

We now have a general procedure for reducing the tensor, C. Of course, the combined state, $\phi\chi$, is represented by only a single element of C. This element can be expanded as a linear combination of those elements of $C', D', \ldots$ which are eigenstates of J_z with eigenvalue $m = m_\phi + m_\chi$. As we remarked at the outset, the coefficients in this expansion are the Clebsch–Gordan coefficients.

We remarked at the beginning of this section that the concept of isospin arises as a generalization of charge independence in nuclear physics. It was, however, introduced simply as a postulate and its truth or falsity must be determined by testing the resultant predictions. We shall therefore conclude with a brief summary of these predictions.

1. Classification

Strongly interacting particles can be classified into isospin multiplets with $2j+1$ states in each multiplet. All members of a multiplet have identical strong interaction properties but differ in their electromagnetic and weak interactions. The existence of one member of a multiplet implies the existence of all other members although it does not, of course, imply that the other members are stable. For instance, the existence of a positively charged proton with $j = \frac{1}{2}$, $m = \frac{1}{2}$ implies the existence of a neutral particle (the neutron) with $j = \frac{1}{2}$, $m = -\frac{1}{2}$. The proton and neutron behave identically in the strong interaction, but the neutron decays into the proton by the weak interaction.

2. Coupling

When two particles interact, the resultant may be described by an element of the tensor which is the direct product of the tensors containing the two interacting particles. It may be reduced in the usual way and the reduced tensor elements are exactly what one would expect from the angular momentum vector coupling rules. For instance, states of isospin 1 and $\frac{1}{2}$ can couple to give isospin $\frac{3}{2}$, or $\frac{1}{2}$. The expansion coefficients are the Clebsch–Gordan coefficients.

3. Isospin conservation

Since the strong interaction is invariant under SU_2 transformations, it follows that its matrix elements are isospin scalars and that it does not connect states of different isospin. A typical matrix element has the form

$$\langle B_{jk...m} | S | A_{jk...m} \rangle, \qquad (4.132)$$

where A, B are irreducible. This implies that both total isospin (a vector quantity) and its third component (a scalar) are conserved in the strong interaction. Also, all strong interaction eigenstates have a definite isospin.

4. Cross sections

The fact that all members of an isospin multiplet have identical strong interaction properties leads to important relations between cross sections. Consider a reaction of the form

$$A + B \rightarrow C + D \qquad (4.133)$$

and let us suppose that it proceeds by the strong interaction. The reaction amplitude can be written as

$$\langle C + D | S | A + B \rangle. \qquad (4.134)$$

Then both the initial and final states can be expanded as linear combinations of eigenstates of j, m. Let us write these eigenstates as ψ_{jm}, ψ'_{jm} respectively. The expansion coefficients are, as usual, the Clebsch–Gordan coefficients. Now the reaction amplitude

$$\langle j \| S \| j \rangle \equiv \langle S_j \rangle \equiv \langle \psi'_{jm} | S | \psi_{jm} \rangle \qquad (4.135)$$

is called a *reduced matrix element* of S. It depends on j, but not on m. And it is related to the amplitude (4.134) by the Clebsch–Gordan coefficients. Now consider a reaction

$$A' + B' \rightarrow C' + D' \qquad (4.136)$$

between some other members of the isospin multiplets which contain A, B, C, D. Once again, the initial and final states can be expanded as linear combinations of the ψ_{jm}, ψ'_{jm} respectively. Hence the reaction amplitude for (4.136) can be expressed in terms of the *same* reduced matrix elements, (4.135), as the reaction amplitude for (4.133). And in each case the expansion coefficients depend only on the Clebsch–Gordan coefficients. This is a special case of the *Wigner–Eckart* theorem which deals with the relations between matrix elements and reduced matrix elements.

TABLE 4.2

Possible states of the pion-nucleon system

	j	m	Clebsch–Gordan coefficient
$\pi^+ p$	$\frac{3}{2}$	$\frac{3}{2}$	1
$\pi^+ n$	$\frac{3}{2}$	$\frac{1}{2}$	$\sqrt{\frac{1}{3}}$
	$\frac{1}{2}$	$\frac{1}{2}$	$\sqrt{\frac{2}{3}}$
$\pi^0 p$	$\frac{3}{2}$	$\frac{1}{2}$	$\sqrt{\frac{2}{3}}$
	$\frac{1}{2}$	$\frac{1}{2}$	$-\sqrt{\frac{1}{3}}$
$\pi^0 n$	$\frac{3}{2}$	$-\frac{1}{2}$	$\sqrt{\frac{2}{3}}$
	$\frac{1}{2}$	$-\frac{1}{2}$	$\sqrt{\frac{1}{3}}$
$\pi^- p$	$\frac{3}{2}$	$-\frac{1}{2}$	$\sqrt{\frac{1}{3}}$
	$\frac{1}{2}$	$-\frac{1}{2}$	$-\sqrt{\frac{2}{3}}$
$\pi^- n$	$\frac{3}{2}$	$-\frac{3}{2}$	1

An example may help to make the point clear. Consider the reactions which can occur in the pion-nucleon system. It can exist in ten different states. Table 4.2 shows the possible values of j, m together with the Clebsch–Gordan coefficients calculated in Section 4.2. These coefficients can be used to express the reaction amplitudes in terms of the reduced matrix elements.

$$\langle \pi^+ p | \pi^+ p \rangle = \langle \pi^- n | \pi^- n \rangle = \langle S_{\frac{3}{2}} \rangle,$$

$$\langle \pi^+ n | \pi^+ n \rangle = \langle \pi^- p | \pi^- p \rangle = \tfrac{1}{3} \langle S_{\frac{3}{2}} \rangle + \tfrac{2}{3} \langle S_{\frac{1}{2}} \rangle,$$

$$\langle \pi^0 p | \pi^+ n \rangle = \langle \pi^0 n | \pi^- p \rangle = \tfrac{1}{3}\sqrt{2} \langle S_{\frac{3}{2}} \rangle - \tfrac{1}{3}\sqrt{2} \langle S_{\frac{1}{2}} \rangle. \quad (4.137)$$

Eqn (4.137) does not include the amplitudes with π^0 in the initial state since these can not be observed experimentally. The reaction cross sections are proportional to the squares of the moduli of these amplitudes. Eqns (4.137) lead to three equalities.

$$\sigma(\pi^+ p \to \pi^+ p) = \sigma(\pi^- n \to \pi^- n) \equiv \sigma_1,$$

$$\sigma(\pi^+ n \to \pi^+ n) = \sigma(\pi^- p \to \pi^- p) \equiv \sigma_2, \quad (4.138)$$

$$\sigma(\pi^+ n \to \pi^0 p) = \sigma(\pi^- p \to \pi^0 n) \equiv \sigma_3.$$

Eqns (4.138) define $\sigma_1, \sigma_2, \sigma_3$. An inequality can also be derived by noticing that

$$|\langle S_{\frac{3}{2}} \rangle|^2 |\langle S_{\frac{1}{2}} \rangle|^2 - |\langle S_{\frac{3}{2}} \rangle \langle S_{\frac{1}{2}} \rangle|^2 \geqslant 0, \quad (4.139)$$

$$\therefore \ 4\sigma_1 \sigma_2 \geqslant (\sigma_1 + \sigma_2 - 2\sigma_3)^2. \quad (4.140)$$

Many other similar relations have been derived and tested. They always hold to a good approximation and any discrepancies can be explained as second-order effects produced by the electromagnetic interaction.

4.6. G-parity

G-parity is a discrete symmetry, but we have not been able to discuss it earlier since its definition uses the concept of isospin. The present section gives the motive for introducing G-parity and then sets out the basic formalism. Now we have already seen that phase conventions are of crucial importance for any discrete symmetry. These conventions are made for convenience but they should not be allowed to obscure the essential physics. For this reason, we have been stressing the distinction between those results which are conventional and convenient and those which lead to empirically testable statements. The situation is unusually complicated for G-parity since a total of three separate phase conventions is needed to define it. We shall argue that there is a natural choice for each convention. However, the choice is made in different ways in the various parts of the literature and it is hoped that an explicit account of this point will help to resolve some of the obscurities and contradictions which are present in other treatments. The essential physics can be summed up in a selection rule which is quite independent of the conventions used.

Let us start by observing that the charge-conjugation operation is a composite inversion. It affects a group of properties which are defined, some by the strong, some by the electromagnetic, and some by the weak interaction. We have seen that it is an exact symmetry for the strong interaction and may well be exact for the electromagnetic interaction also. Thus, if it is considered solely as a symmetry principle, there is no particular reason to discuss its properties separately for the two types of interaction. However, considered as a conservation law or selection rule, it has severe limitations. Charge-conjugation eigenstates must be electrically neutral as well as having zero hypercharge, baryon number and lepton numbers. Thus π^0 is a charge-conjugation eigenstate but π^+, π^- are not. It would be useful to have a selection rule which depended on strong interaction properties only. A larger number of eigenstates would exist and, if one member of an isospin multiplet was an eigenstate, then all other members would also be eigenstates and all would have the same quantum number. π^+, π^0, π^-, for instance, would be treated on an equal footing and it would be possible to derive a selection rule for decay into multi-pion states analogous to the selection rule for decay into multi-photon states (Section 2.3). The selection rule would still, of course, apply only to those states with zero hypercharge, baryon number and lepton numbers. It would be exact for the strong interaction though not, in general, for the electromagnetic and weak interactions.

The trick used is to remember that strong interactions are invariant under SU_2 transformations, that is, 'rotations' in isospin space. However a rotation by π about an axis normal to the z-axis in isospin space changes the sign of J_z and, for states of zero hypercharge, the sign of Q as well. It thus, roughly speaking, inverts the electromagnetic properties but leaves the strong interaction properties unchanged. We therefore define the G-parity operation as this rotation followed by charge conjugation. It achieves something very close to an inversion of the strong interaction properties only leaving the electromagnetic properties unchanged. We emphasize again that although, like any other discrete symmetry operation, G-parity can lead to a symmetry principle as well as a conservation law or selection rule, only the latter provides any new and interesting physics.

So far, it is all straightforward. The next step is to work out this idea mathematically and to write down its physical consequences. By construction, the G-parity operator has interesting consequences only for the isospin part of the state function. A satisfactory account of its properties can therefore be derived by determining how it transforms J_x, J_y, J_z. We treat this in two parts. First consider the rotation in isospin space. Remember that J_x, J_y, J_z obey commutation relations of the form (4.14), (4.65). The constant, α, determines the normalization. It is fixed by the quantization of j and not by SU_2. Its values for angular momentum and isospin are $\frac{1}{2}\hbar$ and $\frac{1}{2}$ respectively. Hence, for isospin,

$$[J_x, J_y] = iJ_z. \tag{4.141}$$

$$J_x = \tfrac{1}{2}\begin{pmatrix} 0 & 1 \\ 1 & 0 \end{pmatrix}, \qquad J_y = \tfrac{1}{2}\begin{pmatrix} 0 & -i \\ i & 0 \end{pmatrix}, \qquad J_z = \tfrac{1}{2}\begin{pmatrix} 1 & 0 \\ 0 & -1 \end{pmatrix}. \tag{4.142}$$

J_x, J_y, J_z are generators of infinitesimal rotations about the x-, y-, z-axes respectively in isospin space. Hence, by an argument analogous to that used when deriving eqns (4.30), (4.74), the operator which produces a rotation by π about the x-axis is

$$T_x(\pi) = \mathrm{e}^{-i\pi J_x} = I \cos\frac{\pi}{2} - 2iJ_x \sin\frac{\pi}{2}$$

$$= \begin{pmatrix} 0 & -i \\ -i & 0 \end{pmatrix}. \tag{4.143}$$

Similarly

$$T_y(\pi) = \begin{pmatrix} 0 & -1 \\ 1 & 0 \end{pmatrix}. \tag{4.144}$$

More generally, a rotation by π about an axis in the (x, y) plane making an angle, ϕ, with the x axis, is given by rotating $T_x(\pi)$ by ϕ about the z-axis.

$$T = T_z(\phi)T_x(\pi)T_z^{-1}(\phi)$$

$$= \begin{pmatrix} \mathrm{e}^{-\frac{1}{2}i\phi} & 0 \\ 0 & \mathrm{e}^{\frac{1}{2}i\phi} \end{pmatrix} \begin{pmatrix} 0 & -i \\ -i & 0 \end{pmatrix} \begin{pmatrix} \mathrm{e}^{\frac{1}{2}i\phi} & 0 \\ 0 & \mathrm{e}^{-\frac{1}{2}i\phi} \end{pmatrix} = \begin{pmatrix} 0 & -i\,\mathrm{e}^{-i\phi} \\ -i\,\mathrm{e}^{i\phi} & 0 \end{pmatrix}, \tag{4.145}$$

where we have used eqn (4.74). Clearly, for the special cases in which $\phi = 0, \pi/2$, eqn (4.145) reduces to eqns (4.143), (4.144) respectively. Consider the physical interpretation of eqn (4.145). It is easy to see that T commutes with J^2 but anti-commutes with J_z. Thus, as we required initially, the total isospin is left unchanged but its third component is reversed. The transformations of J_x, J_y are given by

$$TJ_xT^{-1} = J_x \cos 2\phi + J_y \sin 2\phi,$$

$$TJ_yT^{-1} = J_x \sin 2\phi - J_y \cos 2\phi. \qquad (4.146)$$

It follows that the transformations of the stepping operators are given by

$$TJ_+T^{-1} = J_- \, e^{2i\phi}, \qquad TJ_-T^{-1} = J_+ \, e^{-2i\phi}. \qquad (4.147)$$

The discussion so far gives us no reason to choose any particular value of ϕ in the definition of G. It must be fixed by convention.

Next, consider how J_x, J_y, J_z transform under charge conjugation. Since the charge conjugation operation reverses all charges, it reverses the order of elements in an isospin multiplet and hence the third component of isospin.

$$CJ_zC^{-1} = -J_z. \qquad (4.148)$$

Now, J_x, J_y must remain hermitian and traceless under charge conjugation (cf. discussion in Section 1.2). But any hermitian traceless matrix can be expressed as a linear combination of J_x, J_y, J_z. Hence we can write with full generality

$$CJ_xC^{-1} = a_xJ_x + a_yJ_y + a_zJ_z, \qquad CJ_yC^{-1} = b_xJ_x + b_yJ_y + b_zJ_z, \qquad (4.149)$$

where the a_i, b_i are expansion coefficients. Now, using the commutation relations (4.141),

$$iCJ_xC^{-1} = C[J_y, J_z]C^{-1}$$

$$\therefore \quad a_xJ_x + a_yJ_y + a_zJ_z = b_xJ_y - b_yJ_x$$

$$\therefore \quad a_x = -b_y, \qquad a_y = b_x, \qquad a_z = 0. \qquad (4.150)$$

Similarly

$$b_z = 0, \qquad a_x^2 + a_y^2 = 1. \qquad (4.151)$$

Clearly eqns (4.150), (4.151) have the parametric solution

$$CJ_xC^{-1} = J_x \cos \theta + J_y \sin \theta, \qquad CJ_yC^{-1} = J_x \sin \theta - J_y \cos \theta,$$

$$CJ_+C^{-1} = J_- \, e^{i\theta}, \qquad CJ_-C^{-1} = J_+ \, e^{-i\theta}. \qquad (4.152)$$

where θ is an arbitrary real constant. But these equations have exactly the same form as eqns (4.146), (4.147). Thus the charge-conjugation operator *produces rotation by π about some axis in the x, y plane in isospin space.* The definitions of isospin and charge conjugation are not sufficient to determine which axis must be used. It can be chosen by convention. A natural and convenient convention is the one which requires that the stepping operators, J_+, J_-, change one to the other under charge conjugation:

$$CJ_+C^{-1} = J_-, \qquad CJ_-C^{-1} = J_+. \qquad (4.153)$$

Under this convention $\theta = 0$. In geometrical terms, it means that charge conjugation produces a rotation by π about the x-axis in isospin space.

We are now in a position to define the G-parity operator more precisely. We have already defined it as rotation by π about some axis in the (x, y) plane in isospin space followed by charge conjugation. But we have not defined which axis is to be used.

$$G = CT \qquad (4.154)$$

$$\therefore \quad GJ_+G^{-1} = e^{i\lambda}J_+, \qquad GJ_-G^{-1} = e^{-i\lambda}J_-, \qquad (4.155)$$

$$GJ_xG^{-1} = J_x\cos\lambda + J_y\sin\lambda, \qquad GJ_yG^{-1} = J_x\sin\lambda - J_y\cos\lambda,$$

where

$$\lambda = 2\phi - \theta. \qquad (4.156)$$

Clearly, if we require that all members of an isospin multiplet have the same G-parity, then λ is zero. If θ is zero, then ϕ must be zero also. Thus, with our conventions, the G-parity operation is defined as a rotation by π about the x-axis in isospin space followed by charge conjugation. Three phase conventions are used in this definition. First, the Condon and Shortley phase convention sets α to zero in eqns (4.28), (4.29). This convention defines the x-, y-axes in isospin space. Secondly, the requirement that the stepping operators, J_+, J_-, change one to the other under charge conjugation sets θ to zero in eqns (4.152). This convention states that charge conjugation produces a rotation by π about the x-axis in isospin space. Thirdly, the requirement that all members of an isospin multiplet have the same G-parity sets ϕ to zero in eqns (4.146), (4.147). This convention gives the choice of axis in our definition of G-parity. Now the Condon and Shortley phase convention is used almost universally, but the other two are not. In particular, G-parity is often defined as a rotation by π about the y-axis in isospin space followed by charge conjugation. If this convention is followed then either eqn (4.153) breaks down or the various members of an isospin multiplet have different G-parities. Neither alternative seems particularly desirable. In what follows, we shall illustrate the discussion using our definition of G-parity. It will be seen that the algebra emerges in a natural and logical fashion. We shall then indicate briefly the changes produced by other conventions. The algebra is then less simple but the essential physics is preserved.

We have argued that G-parity can have an eigenvalue only for isospin multiplets which have zero hypercharge, baryon number and lepton number, that is, those which have the quantum numbers of non-strange mesons. Such multiplets have an electrically neutral member which is left invariant by the charge-conjugation operation and can therefore be assigned a charge-conjugation quantum number, β. In the notation of eqn (4.107) et seq.,

$$CA(a, b) = \beta A(a, b) \tag{4.157}$$

for $a = b$. Hence, using eqns (4.80), (4.145), (4.108),

$$GA(a, b) = (-\mathrm{i})^{a+b}\beta A(a, b) = (-1)^{j}\beta A(a, b). \tag{4.158}$$

For states of even isospin the G-parity quantum number is the same as the charge conjugation quantum number of the neutral member. For states of odd isospin it is opposite. Since, by construction, all members of an isospin multiplet have the same behaviour under G-parity, eqn (4.158) applies to all members of the multiplet whether or not a, b are equal. Consider the pion for example. The π^0 has isospin 1 and is an eigenstate of charge conjugation with eigenvalue 1. Hence π^+, π^0, π^- are all eigenstates of G-parity and all have eigenvalue -1. Thus any state which contains only pions is an eigenstate of G-parity and has eigenvalue $+1$ or -1 depending on whether there is an even or odd number of pions. Since strong interactions conserve G-parity, it follows that a strong interaction eigenstate which decays to pions only can decay to an even number of pions or an odd number of pions *but not both*.

The concept of G-parity tells us nothing about protons or neutrons since neither is a charge conjugation eigenstate. However, a proton anti-proton system has zero hypercharge, baryon number and lepton number. It can therefore be an eigenstate of charge conjugation. The eigenvalue can be deduced readily from the empirical fact that p, p̄ have opposite intrinsic parities. (This statement can be made without any conventional assumptions. See discussion of eqn (3.3)). It follows that the parity of a pp̄ system is $(-1)^{l+1}$ where l is the orbital angular momentum. However, since p, p̄ are charge-conjugate states, charge conjugation exchanges both the space and spin parts of the state function of the two particles. It is therefore necessary to consider the space and spin parts of the state function together. The triplet spin state is symmetric and the singlet state is antisymmetric and so the symmetry of the spin part of the state function is $(-1)^{s+1}$. Hence the effect of exchange of both the space and spin parts of the state function may be summed up in the equation

$$C|\mathrm{p\bar{p}}\rangle = (-1)^{l+s}|\mathrm{p\bar{p}}\rangle, \tag{4.159}$$

where s is the total intrinsic spin. Similarly

$$C|\mathrm{n\bar{n}}\rangle = (-1)^{l+s}|\mathrm{n\bar{n}}\rangle. \tag{4.160}$$

Neither state is an isospin eigenstate, but standard methods can be used to choose linear combinations which are isospin eigenstates. With the formalism of eqn (4.110), a nucleon is represented by a covariant vector and, as we shall see in Section 5.1, an anti-nucleon by a contravariant vector. Hence the nucleon anti-nucleon system can be represented by a rank-two tensor:

$$\begin{aligned} \mathrm{p\bar{p}} &= V_1 V^1 \equiv A_1^1, & \mathrm{n\bar{n}} &= V_2 V^2 \equiv A_2^2 \\ \mathrm{p\bar{n}} &= V_1 V^2 \equiv A_1^2, & \mathrm{n\bar{p}} &= V_2 V^1 \equiv A_2^1. \end{aligned} \tag{4.161}$$

Using δ^p, A can be reduced to a triplet with components A_1^2, $(\sqrt{\tfrac{1}{2}})(A_1^1 - A_2^2)$, A_2^1 and a singlet $(\sqrt{\tfrac{1}{2}})(A_1^1 + A_2^2)$ (cf. eqn (4.99)). Note that the singlet member of a wholly covariant SU_2 tensor of rank two is antisymmetric (eqn (4.123)), while the singlet member of a mixed tensor is symmetric. This follows immediately from the fact that the former is extracted using the totally antisymmetric tensor, ϵ, while the latter is extracted by taking the symmetric trace. Each member of the triplet has G-parity $(-1)^{l+s+1}$ and the singlet has G-parity $(-1)^{l+s}$. This rule may be summed up in the equation

$$G|\mathrm{N\bar{N}}\rangle = (-1)^{l+s+j}|\mathrm{N\bar{N}}\rangle, \tag{4.162}$$

where j is the total isospin quantum number and N represents either a neutron or a proton. Using eqn (4.162), it is easy to work out which nucleon anti-nucleon states can decay into an even number of pions and which into an odd number of pions.

Clearly, the essential physics of G-parity is embodied in the selection rule. States of even G-parity can decay only to states of even G-parity. States of odd G-parity can decay only to states of odd G-parity. This result has been derived using certain conventions and it is important to see that it holds even if the conventions are not used. Comparison of eqns (4.28), (4.29), (4.152), (4.155) shows that each convention makes a statement about the phases of the stepping operators. Consider what happens if these conventions are not used. It follows from eqn (4.155) that successive members of an isospin multiplet would have G-parities which differed by a constant phase

$$G(Q) = G(0)\, e^{i\lambda Q}, \tag{4.163}$$

where $G(Q)$ is the G-parity of the member of the multiplet with charge, Q. However, *since charge is absolutely conserved in all interactions*, this freedom makes no difference at all to the selection rule. An initial state of charge, Q, and G-parity, $G(0)$, under our convention decays to final states with charge, Q, and G-parity, $G(0)$, but not to states with G-parity, $-G(0)$. Under the more general rule, (4.163), the initial state would have G-parity, $G(Q)$, and would decay to final states with G-parity, $G(Q)$, but not to states with G-parity, $-G(Q)$. The physical predictions are the same.

However, an example may help to illustrate the way in which the formalism becomes more complicated. We have seen that under our convention π^+, π^0, π^- are all eigenstates of G-parity and all have eigenvalue -1. Some authors prefer to retain eqn (4.153) but to define the G-parity operation as a rotation by π about the *y-axis* in isospin space followed by charge conjugation. Thus $\theta = 0$ but $\phi = \pi/2$. Under this convention π^0 has negative G-parity but π^+, π^- have positive G-parity. An alternative device would discard eqn (4.153) and set θ in eqn (4.152) to π. The charge conjugation operation would then produce a rotation by π about the y-axis in isospin space but either π^+, π^- would not be charge conjugate states or it would be necessary to define the isospin triplet as, say, $|\pi^+\rangle, |\pi^0\rangle, -|\pi^-\rangle$. While all pions would have G-parity -1, this would be purchased at some cost. The reader may well conclude that these alternative conventions are rather clumsy, but it must be emphasized that they do not alter the essential physics. Since charge is conserved, the selection rule is unaffected.

4.7. The time reversal operator

We are now in a position to complete our discussion of the time-reversal operator. In Section 1.5, we showed that the time-reversal operator is anti-unitary and therefore, by eqn (1.111), that it has the form

$$T = UK, \tag{4.164}$$

where U is a unitary operator and K is the complex conjugation operator. Then, in Section 2.1, we showed that the operator, TT, could have eigenvalues $+1$, -1 and we remarked, without proof, that the two cases apply to states with integral and half integral spins respectively. In order to prove this last statement, it is necessary to construct an explicit form for T and we are now in a position to do this. Eqns (2.33) state that T inverts the values of momentum, angular momentum and intrinsic spin. The first two requirements are automatically satisfied by operators of the form (4.164). Momentum, $\mathbf{p}$, is given by

$$\mathbf{p} = -i\hbar\nabla, \tag{4.165}$$

and clearly

$$\mathbf{p}' = K\mathbf{p}K^{-1} = -\mathbf{p}. \tag{4.166}$$

Similarly, angular momentum is given by

$$\mathbf{L} = \mathbf{r} \times \mathbf{p} \tag{4.167}$$

and clearly this is also inverted by the complex conjugation operator, K. Hence the simple requirement that T should be anti-unitary and should not affect the position operator, $\mathbf{r}$, is sufficient to ensure that it satisfies all but one of the defining equations (2.32), (2.33). The exception is the last equation, which describes the transformation of intrinsic spin. It follows that U must act on intrinsic spin only and that it must invert its value. Since, by eqns (1.112),

$$KK = I, \tag{4.168}$$

an immediate corollary is that for spinless particles the eigenvalue of TT must always be $+1$.

Now consider the form of U. It must anti-commute with all the generators, J_x, J_y, J_z, of intrinsic spin. It is clear from eqns (4.48) that of the three, only J_y is purely imaginary. The other two are real and hence are left unchanged by K. It follows that U must satisfy

$$UJ_xU^{-1} = -J_x, \qquad UJ_yU^{-1} = J_y, \qquad UJ_zU^{-1} = -J_z. \tag{4.169}$$

These equations are easily solved to yield

$$U = \begin{pmatrix} 0 & -1 \\ 1 & 0 \end{pmatrix}. \tag{4.170}$$

Comparison with eqn (4.144) shows that this is the operator which produces a rotation by π about the y-axis and a little reflection make t clear that this is precisely the operation which one would expect to produce the transformation (4.169). Thus the time-reversal operation consists of complex conjugation followed by a rotation by π about the y-axis in intrinsic spin space.

Let us now operate with T^2 on the general SU_2 spin tensor. In the notation of eqn (4.107) et seq.

$$[TA](a, b) = (-1)^b A^*(b, a),$$

$$\therefore \quad [T^2 A](a, b) = (-1)^{a+b} A(a, b) = (-1)^{2j} A(a, b); \quad (4.171)$$

where the last step uses eqn (4.108). Hence all SU_2 irreducible spin tensor elements are eigenstates of T^2 with eigenvalues $+1$, -1 depending on whether the total spin is integral or half integral. This completes the proof, begun in Section 2.1, that T^2 provides a superselection rule but that its physical content is the same as that of the law of conservation of statistics.

Problems

1. If the state functions, ϕ, χ, describe a nucleon with spin parallel and anti-parallel to the z-axis respectively, what is the direction of the spin vector for the following states
   (a) $\sqrt{\frac{1}{3}}\{(1+i)\phi + \chi\}$ (b) $\frac{1}{2}\{(1-i)\phi + (1+i)\chi\}$?

2. Derive the Clebsch–Gordan coefficient for $j_1 = j_2 = 1$.

3. Derive the matrix representation of J_x, J_y, J_z for $j = \frac{3}{2}$.

4. Reduce the general SU_2 tensor with elements A^p_{jk}.

5. Consider two irreducible isospin SU_2 tensors with elements A_{jk}, B_{pq}. What is the total isospin of each? Suppose that the two states interact. Write down the resulting state tensor and show that it can be reduced to three irreducible tensors. What is the isospin of each? Show explicitly how each element is composed of combinations of the elements of A and B.

6. Deduce eqn (4.170) from eqn (4.169).

7. The η meson has zero spin and isospin and negative parity. It can decay into two γ-rays. Use this information to show that its G-parity is positive. Now explain why it does not decay into two pions but can decay into three.

THE SYMMETRY SU_3

THE success of SU_2 has led rather naturally to a search for higher symmetries. Just as SU_2 enables us to group states into isospin multiplets and to write down simple relationships between the elements of these multiplets, so the higher symmetries give groupings into still larger multiplets with further useful relationships between their elements. This chapter deals with the most successful of these symmetries, SU_3. It starts by arguing that it is desirable to include strangeness and hypercharge in any scheme of higher symmetries. It shows that they cannot be accommodated in SU_2 and that a natural extension is to SU_3. However, the physical interpretation of SU_3 transformations is much less obvious than the physical interpretation of most of the other transformations which have been discussed in earlier chapters. For this reason, the strategy of the present chapter is to proceed by small steps and to check each step by referring back to the experimental evidence. In the first section, a suitable set of generators is set up and, as far as possible, interpreted physically. Then the methods developed in the last chapter are used to classify the multiplets which are permitted by SU_3 and to determine the quantum numbers of their elements. This step can be checked by examining the systematics of some of the lighter baryons and mesons. This leads to a discussion of those multiplets which are permitted by SU_3, but which have not yet been observed. Most noteworthy of these is the triplet of quarks. The hypothesis that all hadrons are in some sense physically composed of quarks is examined but not supported. The predictions which can be made about the systematics of strong interactions using SU_3 are derived by methods analogous to those used with SU_2. Using the concept of U-spin, predictions can also be made about electromagnetic interactions. The final sections consider symmetry breaking and the fact, at first sight paradoxical, that a great many of the more interesting and important results derived from SU_3 are possible precisely because the symmetry is not exact. This is true of splitting both by the strong and by the electromagnetic interaction. We consider both.

5.1. Hypercharge and strangeness

It is worth emphasizing at the outset that both the motive and approach of the search for higher symmetries are rather different from the motive and approach of isospin theory. In isospin theory we started with a symmetry transformation which had a fairly obvious physical interpretation. We then postulated that the strong interaction was invariant under this transformation. This led naturally to a discussion of the relevant observables and conservation laws. The main motive in the search for higher symmetries is to classify particles into multiplets and to find relations between the properties of the members of each multiplet. In order to do this, one must again construct a symmetry transformation and postulate that, to a first approximation, the strong interaction is invariant under this transformation. However, this time the basic physics is most easily understood in terms of observables, and the approach is through the observables and their conservation laws rather than directly in terms of the symmetry transformation.

This section introduces some of the basic ideas of SU_3. It starts by suggesting an observable which could be used to extend SU_2. It then chooses a suitable set of generators. However, in contrast to SU_2, the choice of generators can not simply be interpreted as the choice of a coordinate system. The range of possibilities is both larger and more arbitrary. However, four of the generators chosen do have an immediate physical interpretation, and the meaning of the others will emerge more clearly later in the chapter. Finally, the allowed SU_3 multiplets are derived and interpreted.

We have seen that the postulate that the strong interaction is invariant under the SU_2 transformation leads to two types of observable. One is total isospin which is conserved in the strong interaction and unchanged by SU_2 transformations. The other is the third component of isospin which is also conserved in the strong interaction but which can be changed by SU_2 transformations. The strong interaction can depend on total isospin but not on its third component. Indeed, without the electromagnetic interaction the third component could not be observed at all. Now we have mentioned that the approach to higher symmetries is through observables. A convenient way to begin a search for such symmetries is to look for an additive observable which could play a part analogous to the part played by the third component of isospin in SU_2 theory. The observable must be strictly conserved in the strong interaction, although not necessarily in the electromagnetic and weak interactions. And to a first approximation the strong interaction must not depend on its value. The latter requirement is much

9

more difficult to express in clear physical terms than the former. However, it obviously rules out such observables as baryon number. The strong interaction of a one-baryon state is quite different from that of a two-baryon state. The observable chosen is hypercharge and the basic idea of SU_3 is that a useful higher symmetry can be constructed by adding hypercharge to isospin.

We start by observing that, in order to give a complete description of an isospin multiplet, it is necessary to state not only the total number of elements in the multiplet (which is given by the isospin) but also what their charges are. We therefore introduce a new quantity, *hypercharge*, defined as twice the mean charge of an isospin multiplet. It follows from this definition that hypercharge always has integral values. A complete description of the charge states of any isospin multiplet can be obtained from the isospin and hypercharge. The charge, Q, of any state is given by

$$Q = \tfrac{1}{2}Y + I_z, \tag{5.1}$$

where Y is hypercharge, and we shall in future distinguish isospin from angular momentum by denoting the former by I and its third component by I_z. I_z can, of course, take any value between $-I$ and I. Values of I and Y for some well known isospin multiplets are

	I	Y
N, K	$\tfrac{1}{2}$	1
Σ, π	1	0
Λ, η	0	0
$\Xi, \overline{K}$	$\tfrac{1}{2}$	-1

For essentially historical reasons, the related quantity *strangeness* is often used instead of hypercharge. Strangeness is defined as hypercharge minus baryon number.

The importance of hypercharge and strangeness springs from the fact that they are both strictly conserved in the strong and electromagnetic interactions, although not in the weak interaction. (The evidence for this statement is fully discussed in the literature. See, for example, Sakurai 1964.) They give additive quantum numbers and so must be associated in the usual way with hermitian operators. Consider how one might try to combine them with isospin. Since all members of a given isospin multiplet have the same hypercharge, the hypercharge operator must commute with all the generators of SU_2. But any additive hermitian operator which can be described within the SU_2 scheme can be written as a linear combination of the generators of SU_2 and no such linear combination can commute with all the generators. It follows that hypercharge cannot be described within SU_2 and hence that, if we want to incorporate isospin and hypercharge into the same scheme, then we must go to a higher symmetry. This higher symmetry will have a larger set of generators, and it must be possible to express hypercharge and the three components of isospin as linear combinations of these generators. A convenient step up from SU_2 is, of course, SU_3 and therefore we try this. At this stage SU_3 is just a very bare hypothesis. It is necessary to give it physical content and see whether it works.

We start by choosing a set of 3×3 linearly independent hermitian traceless matrices to act as the generators of SU_3. It follows immediately from the $n^2 - 1$ rule given in Chapter 4 that there must be eight generators in all. At this stage, the choice of generators is completely arbitrary. We simply require a set which can be used to give isospin and hypercharge in a straightforward way. The following set is convenient:

$$\lambda_1 = \begin{pmatrix} 0 & 1 & 0 \\ 1 & 0 & 0 \\ 0 & 0 & 0 \end{pmatrix} \quad \lambda_2 = \begin{pmatrix} 0 & -i & 0 \\ i & 0 & 0 \\ 0 & 0 & 0 \end{pmatrix} \quad \lambda_3 = \begin{pmatrix} 1 & 0 & 0 \\ 0 & -1 & 0 \\ 0 & 0 & 0 \end{pmatrix}$$

$$\lambda_4 = \begin{pmatrix} 0 & 0 & 1 \\ 0 & 0 & 0 \\ 1 & 0 & 0 \end{pmatrix} \quad \lambda_5 = \begin{pmatrix} 0 & 0 & -i \\ 0 & 0 & 0 \\ i & 0 & 0 \end{pmatrix} \quad \lambda_6 = \begin{pmatrix} 0 & 0 & 0 \\ 0 & 0 & 1 \\ 0 & 1 & 0 \end{pmatrix} \quad (5.2)$$

$$\lambda_7 = \begin{pmatrix} 0 & 0 & 0 \\ 0 & 0 & -i \\ 0 & i & 0 \end{pmatrix} \quad \lambda_8 = \sqrt{\tfrac{1}{3}} \begin{pmatrix} 1 & 0 & 0 \\ 0 & 1 & 0 \\ 0 & 0 & -2 \end{pmatrix}.$$

From these eight generators it is possible to construct any SU_3 transformation. Now the first three matrices are just the Pauli spin matrices with an extra row and column of zeros added. This gives a natural choice for the isospin operators by analogy with eqn (4.142)

$$I_x = \tfrac{1}{2}\lambda_1, \qquad I_y = \tfrac{1}{2}\lambda_2, \qquad I_z = \tfrac{1}{2}\lambda_3. \qquad (5.3)$$

Next we need an operator for hypercharge. It must be a 3×3 hermitian traceless matrix which commutes with I_x, I_y, I_z. The only matrix satisfying this condition is

$$Y = C \begin{pmatrix} 1 & 0 & 0 \\ 0 & 1 & 0 \\ 0 & 0 & -2 \end{pmatrix}, \qquad (5.4)$$

where C is a real constant. This is as far as we can go by SU_3 alone. There is no reason to choose any particular value for C. It must be given by experiment. We shall state the result now and justify it later. Only the value $C = \frac{1}{3}$ successfully predicts all multiplets which have been found to exist. Hence

$$Y = \sqrt{\tfrac{1}{3}}\lambda_8. \tag{5.5}$$

Now if λ_1, λ_2, λ_3, λ_8 were the only generators of SU_3, then it would have no more physical content than SU_2 and conservation of hypercharge taken together. The distinctive addition needed to complete the symmetry scheme is contained in the generators λ_4–λ_7. It will become clear presently that the choice, (5.2), for these generators is a convenient one. At present, we simply remark that they are obtained from λ_1, λ_2 by permuting rows and columns. The final observable which we need at this stage is charge. This can be derived immediately using eqns (5.1), (5.3), (5.5).

$$Q = \tfrac{1}{2}(\lambda_8/\sqrt{3}+\lambda_3) = \tfrac{1}{3}\begin{pmatrix} 2 & 0 & 0 \\ 0 & -1 & 0 \\ 0 & 0 & -1 \end{pmatrix}. \tag{5.6}$$

All strong interaction eigenstates are eigenstates of I_z, Y, Q. Note that the operators corresponding to all three observables are diagonal.

The next step is to classify the multiplets which are permitted by SU_3 and to determine the quantum numbers of their elements. In SU_3, as in SU_2, multiplets can be written as irreducible tensors. As we saw in Section 4.4, an irreducible SU_3 tensor is totally symmetric in both upper and lower indices and has all traces zero. SU_3 differs from SU_2 in that each index can take the values one, two, or three, and that we do not have the simplifying result found for SU_2 that only lower indices are needed. The general SU_3 irreducible tensor has U upper and L lower indices. We shall discuss the reduction of tensors in some detail in Section 5.4. For the rest of the present section, we shall be concerned with the properties of tensors which have already been reduced.

First, let us calculate the number of elements in each multiplet. This number is called the *dimension* of the multiplet. The requirement of total symmetry means that we are not concerned with the order of the indices but merely with the total number of ones, twos, and threes amongst both upper and lower indices. Consider the lower indices. Let there be p ones. Then there will be $L-p$ twos and threes. The number, n say, of twos may then be chosen in $L-p+1$ ways and the number,

λ say, of threes will be $L-n-p$. Thus the total number of possibilities for the lower indices is

$$N_L = \sum_{p=0}^{L} (L-p+1) = \tfrac{1}{2}(L+1)(L+2).　　　　(5.7)$$

Similarly

$$N_U = \tfrac{1}{2}(U+1)(U+2).　　　　(5.8)$$

The total number of possibilities is $N_L N_U$ less the number of trace equations. Now each trace equation has the form

$$\delta_j^p A_{pq...t}^{jk...l} = 0,　　　　(5.9)$$

and there must clearly be $N_{(L-1)}N_{(U-1)}$ of these. Hence the total dimension is

$$D = N_L N_U - N_{(L-1)}N_{(U-1)} = \tfrac{1}{2}(L+1)(U+1)(L+U+2).　　　　(5.10)$$

Multiplets are often referred to by their dimensions. We can immediately write down the dimensions of the first few:

S	1		
A_j	3	A^j	$\overline{3}$
A_{jk}	6	A^{jk}	$\overline{6}$
A_j^p	8		
A_{jkl}	10	A^{jkl}	$\overline{10}.$

The bar distinguishes covariant from contravariant tensors.

Next, we need to know the quantum numbers of all the elements of each multiplet. As before, let us denote the numbers of ones, twos, and threes among the lower indices by p, n, λ respectively, and the numbers among the upper indices by p', n', λ' respectively. Then the general tensor element may be written $A(p, n, \lambda, p', n', \lambda')$. This notation is rather cumbersome and it is often convenient to abbreviate it to $A(\mu)$ where μ is a shorthand for $p, n, \lambda, p', n', \lambda'$. Using eqns (4.85), (5.3), (5.5), (5.6) it is easy to prove the following important relationships:

$$[I_z A](\mu) = \tfrac{1}{2}(p - n - p' + n')A(\mu),　　　　(5.11)$$

$$[YA](\mu) = \{\tfrac{1}{3}(L-U) - \lambda + \lambda'\} A(\mu),　　　　(5.12)$$

$$[QA](\mu) = \{\tfrac{1}{3}(U-L) + p - p'\} A(\mu),　　　　(5.13)$$

where we have used

$$n + p + \lambda = L, \qquad n' + p' + \lambda' = U.　　　　(5.14)$$

We have remarked that upper and lower indices are not equivalent in SU_3. However, it follows readily from eqns (5.11–13) that their properties are closely related. A given index makes opposite contributions to the additive quantum numbers depending on whether it is covariant or contravariant. For instance A^3_1 has $Q = Y = 1, I_z = \frac{1}{2}$ but A^1_3 has $Q = Y = -1, I_z = -\frac{1}{2}$. This property suggests a natural way to relate the tensor elements representing particles and anti-particles. If a particle is represented by an element of a tensor, A, given by

$$A^{jk\ldots m}_{pq\ldots t}$$

(cf. eqn (4.78)), then the corresponding anti-particle can be represented by an element of the hermitian conjugate tensor, $A^\dagger$, given by

$$A^{*pq\ldots t}_{jk\ldots m}. \tag{5.15}$$

Hermitian conjugation consists of exchange of upper and lower indices followed by complex conjugation. This is, of course, a straightforward generalization of eqn (1.51). We shall see presently, for instance, that the proton can be represented by the element, A^3_1, of a rank-two tensor. The anti-proton can be represented by the element, A^{*1}_3, of the hermitian conjugate tensor.

Eqn (5.13) has the further striking consequence that any state has an integral electric charge if, and only if, $U - L$ is an exact multiple of three. Since fractional electric charges have never been observed, this implies that only

$$S, A^p_j, A_{jkl}, A^{jkl}$$

of the irreducible tensors listed above can correspond to observed multiplets. Thus quantization of charge gives a restriction *in addition* to the normal restrictions of SU_3. The latter permits some multiplets which may not exist physically. In particular, the triplet, A_j, does not appear to exist. The position is in sharp contrast with SU_2 for which *all* the low ranking states are found in nature and for which the entire symmetry scheme can be obtained by considering combinations of elementary doublets. We return to this question later.

Next consider the total isospin, I. I^2 commutes with all the generators of SU_2 and hence all members of a given SU_2 multiplet are eigenstates of I^2, and all have the same eigenvalue. This is not true for SU_3. Most SU_3 multiplets contain several isospin multiplets. In fact, it was the possibility that the properties of several isospin multiplets might be related in some useful way which provided the basic motive for introducing SU_3. The operation of I^2 on the general SU_3 tensor may be derived by the standard method.

$$[I^2A](\mu) = \tfrac{1}{4}\{(p+n)(p+n+2) + (p'+n')(p'+n'+2) - 2(p-n)(p'-n')\}$$
$$\times A(\mu) - pp'A(p-1,\, n+1,\, \lambda,\, p'-1,\, n'+1,\, \lambda')$$
$$- nn'A(p+1,\, n-1,\, \lambda,\, p'+1,\, n'-1,\, \lambda'). \tag{5.16}$$

This rather cumbersome expression has several striking features. First, it is clear that if the tensor has lower indices only, $U = 0$, then the total isospin is given by the familiar expression

$$[I^2A](\mu) = \tfrac{1}{4}(p+n)(p+n+2)A(\mu) \tag{5.17}$$

cf. eqns (4.108), (4.109). Similarly, if it has upper indices only,

$$[I^2A](\mu) = \tfrac{1}{4}(p'+n')(p'+n'+2)A(\mu). \tag{5.18}$$

However, if *both* upper *and* lower indices are present then the expression is more complex and it is clear that not every eigenstate of SU_3 is necessarily an eigenstate of I^2. Now, of course, in practice all states which exist physically are eigenstates of I^2, at least up to the level of electromagnetic corrections. Eqn (5.16) simply implies that in certain cases it might be necessary to choose suitable linear combinations of the basic SU_3 states in order to satisfy this condition. Once again it is clear that not every state which is consistent with SU_3 is necessarily to be found in nature.

We remarked at the outset that the basic postulate of SU_2 leads to two very distinct types of observable. One, I_z, is an additive observable which can be changed by suitable SU_2 transformations. The SU_3 observables in this class are I_z, Y, Q. The other, I^2, has a more complicated behaviour when two states are combined and is invariant under all SU_2 transformations. All members of an SU_2 multiplet are eigenstates of I^2 and all have the same eigenvalue. Irreducible tensors corresponding to multiplets with different eigenvalues of I^2 can be distinguished by their *rank*. It should now be clear that an analogous situation exists for SU_3. The quantum numbers, U, L, which give the numbers of upper and lower indices in an irreducible SU_3 tensor are invariant under all SU_3 transformations. All members of an SU_3 multiplet are eigenstates of U, L and all have the same eigenvalues. These quantum numbers allow us to label irreducible SU_3 multiplets without ambiguity. They are closely related to the so-called Casimir operators. (See, for example, de Swart 1966).

This completes the basic theory of SU_3. The next two sections discuss several specific multiplets and their quantum numbers.

5.2. Multiplets and weight diagrams

The next two sections consider some specific multiplets and their quantum numbers. In doing so, they illustrate many of the ideas developed in the last section. We have seen that not all states which are consistent with SU_3 can exist physically. Some multiplets are entirely composed of states with fractional electric charge and no such states have yet been observed. Some multiplets contain elements which are not eigenstates of total isospin. It is necessary to take suitable linear combinations of these elements in order to form the states which are observed empirically. In the present section, we restrict attention to those states which are permitted, not only by SU_3, but also by charge quantization. First, the quantum numbers of the three lowest ranking multiplets are derived and discussed. In the course of this discussion, it is necessary to reduce a rank-two tensor, and also to form isospin eigenstates by taking suitable linear combinations of the basic SU_3 states. Secondly, the discussion is generalized to include irreducible tensors of any rank. Weight diagrams are introduced as a useful device for representing the quantum numbers of their elements. In the following section we shall consider those multiplets which are permitted by SU_3, but not by charge quantization.

At the end of the last section we listed the four lowest ranking multiplets which are consistent with charge quantization. First came the singlet, S. This is a scalar and therefore invariant under all SU_3 transformations. It follows from eqn (4.84) that it must be an eigenstate of all SU_3 hermitian traceless operators, and that all eigenvalues must be zero. In particular, isospin, charge, and hypercharge are all zero.

Next came the octet, with elements A_j^p. This is a tensor of rank two. The two indices, j, p, can both run from one to three, but since A is irreducible there is the additional restriction that its trace must be zero.

$$\delta_p^j A_j^p = A_p^p = 0. \tag{5.19}$$

This means that the multiplet can have only eight independent elements. In other words, the general tensor, A, can be reduced to an irreducible octet, plus a singlet which can be represented by the trace of the general tensor.

$$S = \sqrt{\tfrac{1}{3}}(A_1^1 + A_2^2 + A_3^3). \tag{5.20}$$

The factor $\sqrt{\frac{1}{3}}$ is a normalization constant. Notice that this singlet is a *symmetric* combination of SU_3 rank-two tensor elements, while the singlet (4.124) is an *antisymmetric* combination of SU_2 rank-two tensor elements. The difference arises because the SU_2 tensor is wholly covariant while the SU_3 tensor is partly contravariant (c.f. discussion of eqn (4.161)). The scalar component of a mixed SU_2 rank-two tensor is also symmetric.

$$S = \sqrt{\frac{1}{2}}(A_1^1 + A_2^2). \qquad (5.21)$$

(Remember that each SU_2 contravariant index can be put into one-to-one correspondence with a covariant index using the antisymmetric tensor, ϵ.)

In order to understand the irreducible octet, let us first use eqns (5.11–15) to write down the quantum numbers for the elements of the general rank-two tensor, A. These are given in Table 5.1. Six of these

TABLE 5.1

Quantum numbers of the elements of a mixed
SU_3 rank-two tensor

	I_z	Y	Q	I^2
A_1^1	0	0	0	—
A_1^2	1	0	1	2
A_1^3	$\frac{1}{2}$	1	1	$\frac{3}{4}$
A_2^1	-1	0	-1	2
A_2^2	0	0	0	—
A_2^3	$-\frac{1}{2}$	1	0	$\frac{3}{4}$
A_3^1	$-\frac{1}{2}$	-1	-1	$\frac{3}{4}$
A_3^2	$\frac{1}{2}$	-1	0	$\frac{3}{4}$
A_3^3	0	0	0	0

states are readily understood and may be assigned immediately as elements of the irreducible octet. The remaining three states must be grouped in suitable linear combinations. The first such combination has already been separated out as an SU_3 singlet, (5.20). The other two form the remaining elements of the octet. Now they must, of course, be isospin eigenstates but eqn (5.16) gives

$$[I^2 A]_1^1 = A_1^1 - A_2^2, \qquad [I^2 A]_2^2 = A_2^2 - A_1^1. \qquad (5.22)$$

Clearly, isospin eigenstates can be constructed as follows:

$$\sqrt{\tfrac{1}{2}}(A_1^1 - A_2^2) \quad \text{with} \quad I(I+1) = 2, \tag{5.23}$$

$$\sqrt{\tfrac{1}{2}}(A_1^1 + A_2^2) \quad \text{with} \quad I(I+1) = 0. \tag{5.24}$$

Note that the isospin singlet is again a symmetrical combination of tensor elements while the isospin triplet is antisymmetric. The state (5.23) is linearly independent of (5.20) and can be included immediately in the octet. The state (5.24) is not, as it stands, linearly independent of (5.20). However, it has the same quantum numbers as A_3^3 and may therefore be combined with A_3^3 in such a way that the combination is independent of (5.20). It is easy to see that the required combination is

$$\sqrt{\tfrac{1}{6}}(A_1^1 + A_2^2 - 2A_3^3). \tag{5.25}$$

We have thus grouped the nine components of the unreduced tensor, A, into an irreducible octet and a singlet, and have arranged that the members of the octet should all be eigenstates of isospin. The irreducible octet contains the following elements

$$A_1^3, A_2^3; \qquad A_1^2, (\sqrt{\tfrac{1}{2}})(A_1^1 - A_2^2), A_2^1; \qquad (\sqrt{\tfrac{1}{6}})(A_1^1 + A_2^2 - 2A_3^3);$$

$$A_3^2, A_3^1.$$

These can be grouped into isospin multiplets with

$$(I, Y) = (\tfrac{1}{2}, 1), (1, 0), (0, 0), (\tfrac{1}{2}, -1). \tag{5.26}$$

The singlet has just one element (5.25), with $I = Y = 0$.

It is customary to display the elements of an SU_3 multiplet on a plot of Y against I_z known as a 'weight diagram'. This makes it easy to see at a glance the quantum numbers of all members of a given multiplet. It will also allow us to discuss the SU_2 sub-groups of SU_3 in a symmetrical way and will lead to a useful rule for taking the direct product of

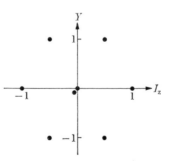

Fig. 5.1. Weight diagram for the octet.

two multiplets. The weight diagram for the octet is given in Fig. 5.1, and the physical states listed in Section 5.1 can be grouped into two octets with the weight diagrams given in Fig. 5.2.

Next comes the decuplet, with elements A_{jkl}. This is a wholly covariant tensor of rank three. Each index can run from 1 to 3, but since A is irreducible it must be totally symmetric, and this limits the number of independent elements to ten. For the decuplet, the eigenvalue equations, (5.11–13), (5.17), lead to particularly simple formulae

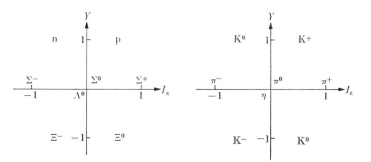

FIG. 5.2. Weight diagrams for the $J^P = \frac{1}{2}^+$ baryon octet and $J^P = 0^-$ meson octet

for the quantum numbers:

$$I = \tfrac{1}{2}(p+n),\, I_z = \tfrac{1}{2}(p-n),\, Y = 1-\lambda,\, Q = p-1, \quad (5.27)$$

where

$$p+n+\lambda = 3. \quad (5.28)$$

These equations give an immediate relationship between I and Y

$$I = 1+\tfrac{1}{2}Y. \quad (5.29)$$

The decuplet therefore consists of four isospin multiplets with

$$(I,\, Y) = (\tfrac{3}{2},\, 1),\, (1,\, 0),\, (\tfrac{1}{2},\, -1),\, (0,\, -2). \quad (5.30)$$

The associated weight diagram is given in Fig. 5.3 and a group of physical states which form a decuplet is given in Fig. 5.4. The notation here is conventional. The symbols N, Y, Ξ, Ω denote baryons with $Y = 1, 0, -1, -2$ respectively.

The reader may perhaps wonder how a group of states which form a multiplet can be distinguished from a fortuitous collection of particles which happen to have the right quantum numbers. Clearly, all properties corresponding to operators which can be expressed in terms of the

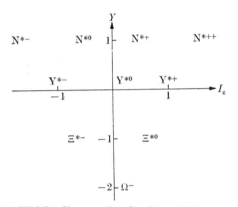

FIG. 5.3. Weight diagram for the decuplet.

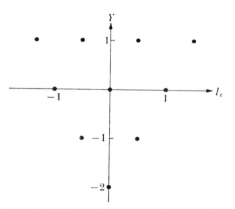

FIG. 5.4. Weight diagram for the $J^P = \frac{3}{2}^+$ baryon octet.

SU_3 generators can be calculated using standard SU_3 algebra. If SU_3 were an exact symmetry, then all other properties (mass, spin, parity, baryon number and so on) would be the same for all members of any given multiplet and identification would be completely straightforward. In fact, as we shall see later, SU_3 is only an approximate symmetry and therefore properties such as mass, which can take a continuous range of values, are not constant for each multiplet. Fortunately it turns out that they vary systematically and can be calculated using first order perturbation theory. Thus SU_3 relates *all* properties of the members of a multiplet and, at least for longer-lived states, there is usually quite enough information to assign particles unambiguously to multiplets. Symmetry breaking is discussed in Sections (5.6), (5.7) and some examples are given there. For the time being, however, we assume that SU_3 is exact and explore the consequences of this assumption. The fact that we can immediately find the three multiplets shown in Figs. 5.2, 5.4, and that the elements of these multiplets have the predicted SU_3 quantum numbers and common spins, parities, and baryon numbers, forms the first part of the justification for SU_3 and, in particular, for our choice of $C = \frac{1}{3}$ in eqn (5.4). In fact, the first really striking success for SU_3 came when the first nine elements of the decuplet were known and Gell-Mann was able to predict the existence and properties of the tenth—the Ω^-. It was a measure of the power of SU_3 that it could be used to predict not only all the discrete quantum numbers of the new particle, but also such continuously variable properties as mass and magnetic dipole moment. Most of these quantum numbers and properties could be checked using the very first event to be observed.

We have mentioned that weight diagrams provide a convenient pictorial method for displaying the quantum numbers of SU_3 multiplets. They can also be used to describe some of their symmetry properties and to calculate direct products. Before proceeding further, we derive a general rule for constructing them. We start by noticing that, for $U = 0$, eqns (5.12), (5.17) yield particularly simple results.

$$Y = \tfrac{1}{3}L - \lambda, \qquad I = \tfrac{1}{2}(L - \lambda), \tag{5.31}$$

where λ runs from 0 to L. For each value of Y, there is a single isospin multiplet and the whole SU_3 multiplet contains

$$(I, Y) = (\tfrac{1}{2}L, \tfrac{1}{3}L), (\tfrac{1}{2}L - \tfrac{1}{2}, \tfrac{1}{3}L - 1), \ldots, (0, -\tfrac{2}{3}L). \tag{5.32}$$

The weight diagram is an inverted triangle with $L + 1$ elements along each side. The decuplet is, of course, a special case of this rule. Similarly, for $L = 0$,

$$(I, Y) = (0, \tfrac{2}{3}U), (\tfrac{1}{2}, \tfrac{2}{3}U - 1), \ldots, (\tfrac{1}{2}U, -\tfrac{1}{3}U). \tag{5.33}$$

The weight diagram is an upright triangle with $U + 1$ elements along each side.

We next extend these results to the general case. First, notice that when L, U, λ, λ' are fixed, the permitted states form an SU_2 multiplet with isospin equal to half the number of indices occupied by ones and twos:

$$I = \tfrac{1}{2}(p + n + p' + n') = \tfrac{1}{2}(L + U - \lambda - \lambda'), \tag{5.34}$$

cf. eqn (4.108). Strictly speaking, we are here imposing SU_2 as well as

SU_3. We have already had to do this once before when discussing the octet. Now from eqn (5.12)

$$Y = \tfrac{1}{3}(L-U) - \lambda + \lambda'. \tag{5.35}$$

For each value of Y, I has a minimum value when either λ or λ' has a maximum value: $\lambda = L$ or $\lambda' = U$. Similarly, I has a maximum value when λ, λ' have their minimum values: either λ or λ' must be zero. Secondly, notice that I, Y are left unchanged when L, U, λ, λ' are all increased by one unit. Thus *all* isospin multiplets in the L, U weight diagram are reproduced in the $L+1$, $U+1$ weight diagram. However, in the latter case, for each value of Y the maximum possible value of I is increased by one unit and so there will be one new multiplet. Similarly, the maximum possible value of Y is increased from $\tfrac{1}{3}(2U+L)$ to $\tfrac{1}{3}(2U+L)+1$. This introduces a new multiplet with $I = \tfrac{1}{2}(L+1)$. And the minimum possible value of Y is decreased from $-\tfrac{1}{3}(2L+U)$ to $-\tfrac{1}{3}(2L+U)-1$. This introduces a new multiplet with $I = \tfrac{1}{2}(U+1)$.

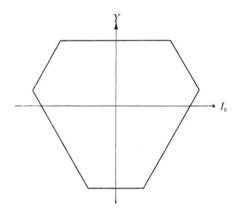

FIG. 5.5. Outline shape of typical weight diagram.

In short, to convert the L, U weight diagram to the $L+1$, $U+1$ weight diagram, add one point to each of the previously populated points and in addition add a ring of points around the perimeter. This process preserves a three-fold symmetry and a typical weight diagram is shaped like Fig. 5.5, where the top row has $L+1$ points and the bottom row has $U+1$ points. By putting this argument into reverse, we can give a general rule for constructing weight diagrams. First draw the outline of the diagram and put an element on every lattice point. Next, inspect the diagram to see whether it is triangular, that is whether either the top or the bottom row contains only one point. If it is triangular then the construction is complete. If not, put an element on every lattice point except those on the perimeter. If the latter set of points forms a triangle, then the construction is complete. If not, continue the process, working steadily inwards until the innermost set of points is either triangular or has contracted to a single point. Some examples of weight diagrams are given in Fig. 5.6. The reader should check that they can be constructed according to this rule.

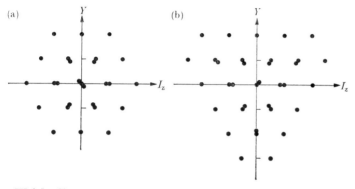

FIG. 5.6. Weight diagrams for multiplets with (a) $L = U = 2$, (b) $L = 4$, $U = 1$.

5.3. Quarks

This section discusses those multiplets which are permitted by SU_3 but not by charge quantization. It starts by recapitulating the theoretical arguments which predict states with one-third integral charge and then explains why the elementary triplet of quarks is particularly interesting. In particular, it attempts to assess the status of the quark model of elementary particles. Next it reviews the present experimental position and the conclusions which can be drawn from the fact that it is extremely difficult, if not impossible, to produce isolated states of non-integral charge. Finally it summarizes the various conclusions which might be drawn as the result of future work.

Let us start by noticing that there is one respect in which SU_3 is rather less satisfactory than SU_2. We have seen that SU_2 allows isospin multiplets to have any integral or half-integral values of I, and that, in point of fact, examples of all the lowest ranking multiplets have been observed. SU_3 allows multiplets to have any integral values of L, U, but so far the only ones which have been observed are the singlet, the octet, and the decuplet. Some of the lowest ranking multiplets of all, including the rank-one triplet, have never been found. The reason for this is not too hard to discover. Eqn (5.13) implies that, unless $U - L$ is an exact multiple of three, the elements of the multiplet have non-integral charge. It appears, then, that charge quantization implies a restriction on possible states *in addition* to the restrictions implied by SU_3, and that for this reason a number of states permitted by the latter cannot exist. Now there is no real reason why this should cause concern. Symmetry principles simply impose restrictions and the fact that one principle is satisfied by no means implies that all others must be satisfied also. The fact that a postulated interaction conserves baryon number, for instance, does not imply that it also conserves charge. Equally, we have already met with one instance in which SU_3 symmetry *on its own* is not sufficient to specify which states exist. When discussing the octet, we obtained eqns (5.23), (5.24) by requiring that physical states must satisfy SU_2 as well as SU_3. Without this requirement, any linear combination of the two would have been possible. In fact, it might reasonably be argued that charge quantization has been known (although not, perhaps, understood) by physicists for so long that the fact that SU_3 does not require it is simply a small, but not particularly disconcerting, sign of the incompleteness of the latter.

Nevertheless, there has been an enormous revival of interest in charge quantization and an intensive experimental search for states with one-third integral charge. There are two basic motives, not always clearly distinguished. First, the behaviour of strongly-interacting states with non-integral charge would in itself make a very interesting study. A comparison between the properties of states with integral and non-integral charge should yield considerable insight into the physics of both. Assuming conservation of charge, at least one state with charge $(m + \frac{1}{3})e$ and one with charge $(m + \frac{2}{3})e$, where m is an integer and e is the electronic charge, must be completely stable against decay. Other superselection rules, for instance conservation of baryon number, could well imply the existence of a whole family of stable states. These states could also, presumably, be bound stably to nuclei. This stability is important since it implies that, even if these states were never produced very abundantly, it would still be possbile to separate them from ordinary matter and perform experiments on them. Charge, for instance, could be determined by a refinement of Millikan's experiment if even one such particle could be trapped on an oil drop.

But there is a second and very powerful motive for searching in particular for members of elementary triplets. These would not only have third-integral charge, but also could be expected to play in SU_3 a part analogous to that played by the nucleon doublet in SU_2. However, since it is necessary to consider upper and lower indices separately, there would in fact be at least two basic triplets—the covariant triplet with elements V_j known as 'quarks', and the contravariant triplet with elements V^j, which would be their anti-particles and are known as 'anti-quarks'. Their quantum numbers follow immediately from eqns (5.11–13), (5.16) and are given in Table 5.2. Such triplets would provide a useful and natural starting point for a discussion of SU_3

TABLE 5.2

Quantum numbers of quarks and anti-quarks

	I_z	Y	Q	I
V_1	$\frac{1}{2}$	$\frac{1}{3}$	$\frac{2}{3}$	$\frac{1}{2}$
V_2	$-\frac{1}{2}$	$\frac{1}{3}$	$-\frac{1}{3}$	$\frac{1}{2}$
V_3	0	$-\frac{2}{3}$	$-\frac{1}{3}$	0
V^1	$-\frac{1}{2}$	$-\frac{1}{3}$	$-\frac{2}{3}$	$\frac{1}{2}$
V^2	$\frac{1}{2}$	$-\frac{1}{3}$	$\frac{1}{3}$	$\frac{1}{2}$
V^3	0	$\frac{2}{3}$	$\frac{1}{3}$	0

symmetry. One could construct multiplets with the SU_3 quantum numbers of observed multiplets in a simple way out of these triplets, just as one constructs nuclear isospin multiplets out of neutrons and protons. This does not, of course, imply that the observed multiplets actually consist of combinations of triplets. We emphasize again that the algebra of SU_3 is exactly the same whether these triplets do or do not exist.

However, it is a relatively small conceptual jump from this position to the hypothesis that strongly-interacting particles are *actually con-structed* of quarks. The observed SU_3 symmetry of strong-interaction physics would then reflect the properties of the quarks themselves. This extreme quark hypothesis is very strong. It asserts that quarks are in some sense truly elementary. If it were to be proved, then one would have made the last step in a sequence of explanations of the properties of matter in terms of entities ever more basic. The search for this kind of simplicity at a fundamental level provided much of the stimulus for early work in particle physics. It seemed that nuclear matter might be composed of a few elementary particles and that nuclear physics might be explained entirely in terms of their interactions and properties.

As the number of 'elementary' particles increased, this project became less attractive and more emphasis was laid on such schemes as SU_3 which gave *relations* between the properties of various particles. The known particles were then on an approximately equal footing, none being regarded as intrinsically more elementary than the others. The extreme quark hypothesis would take the search one level further. Particles with integral charge would be treated as composite objects composed of quarks. Their additive quantum numbers could be deduced when one had found out which quarks were present and such other properties as mass, spin, parity, and magnetic dipole moment would follow from the dynamical states and interaction potential of these quarks. Quarks, in short, would bear much the same relationship to particles with integral charge as neutrons and protons do to the nucleus.

We emphasize again that this extreme quark hypothesis is very strong. In order to establish it experimentally, one would have to do much more than simply detect states with non-integral charge. It is perfectly possible that such states exist, but that other particles are not composed of them. This is the situation in SU_2. Various SU_2 doublets are known to exist; the neutron proton doublet is an example. But one does not claim that all other SU_2 multiplets are made of neutrons and protons. However, if we *do* make the extreme quark hypothesis, then it is immediately possible to determine most of the physical properties which the quarks must have. Baryon number can be fixed by noticing that the elements, A_{jkl}, of the decuplet have unit baryon number and can most simply be explained by assuming that they contain three quarks. Thus the quarks have baryon number $\frac{1}{3}$ and of course the antiquarks have baryon number $-\frac{1}{3}$. (This argument is given more formally in the next section.) The members of the meson octet have baryon number zero and can be explained naturally as quark antiquark states. Spin and parity are rather more difficult to deduce since they depend on the dynamical states of the quarks in observed particles. However, for the lightest particles they are presumably in relative S states. In this case, if quarks have spin $\frac{1}{2}$ and positive parity then the lightest baryons (three-quark states) would have spin $\frac{1}{2}$ or $\frac{3}{2}$ and positive parity. This is what is observed. Anti-baryons would be three anti-quark states and the fact that anti-baryons have negative parity implies that anti-quarks have negative parity also. Given this assignment, one would expect the lightest mesons (quark–anti-quark states) to have spin zero or one and negative parity. This, too, is observed. With the same assumption about dynamical states it is then possible to determine the intrinsic magnetic dipole moments of quarks from the observed magnetic dipole moments of familiar particles. Once again, a consistent and compelling picture emerges. Quite clearly, the extreme quark hypothesis is useful even if only as an heuristic device. However, we shall see presently that all these predictions about spin, parity, and magnetic dipole moment are already implicit in SU_3 and SU_6. Thus the fact that they are correct gives no evidence for the existence of physical quarks.

There remains, however, one important property which we have been unable to predict and that is mass. The relationship between quark masses and observed particle masses depends not only on the dynamical states of quarks, but also on the nature of the forces between them. Since they have been invented in order to explain some of the symmetry properties of the strong interaction, it is reasonable to assume that the forces are the familiar strong forces. One already has a good deal of insight into these forces from the systematics of nuclear structure. In particular, the observed nuclear binding energy is a few MeV per nucleon and very much smaller than the nucleon mass. The extreme quark hypothesis suggests that the mass of an observed particle is the mass of the constituent quarks plus the difference between their kinetic energy and binding energy. For the lightest states, one would expect that both the kinetic and binding energies would be small compared with the particle masses. The latter would to a first approximation be equal to the masses of the constituent quarks. But at this point a difficulty arises. The nucleon, which is considered as a three-quark system, has a mass of about 1000 MeV/c^2 while the pion, which is considered as a quark–anti-quark system, has a mass of only about 140 MeV/c^2. Thus, either binding energy or kinetic energy must play a decisive role in determining the masses of these particles. Either is possible, and *ad hoc* schemes are fairly easy to construct, but either would detract seriously from the essential simplicity of the scheme. This is the first major difficulty with the extreme quark hypothesis.

The second major difficulty concerns the symmetry of quark state functions. Since baryons have half-integral spin, it follows that they cannot be constructed from quarks of integral spin. Quarks must therefore be fermions, and state functions consisting of identical quarks must be totally antisymmetric. Now consider the N^{*++} shown in Fig. 5.4. It follows from the quantum numbers shown in Table 5.2 that, in the extreme quark model, it must consist of three identical V_1 quarks.

But all members of the decuplet are totally symmetric under permutation of indices and thus, in the extreme quark model, they are totally symmetric under exchange of quarks! Thus in this model we should have to postulate that quarks have the spin of fermions, but the symmetry of bosons.

The third major difficulty is that, despite intensive searches, no convincing evidence has been brought forward to suggest that particles with non-integral charge exist. Three types of search have been carried out. First and most important are the searches using conventional accelerators. These would have been successful if the quarks had masses less than about two nucleon masses and were produced with the abundances observed for other particles of the same mass. The fact that they have failed implies either that the quark mass and quark binding energies are of the same order and very large, or that some additional factor is inhibiting quark production. In the absence of direct evidence, neither hypothesis is very plausible.

The second type of search uses the fact that the lightest fractionally-charged particles would be stable. If they are produced by the cosmic irradiation of the upper atmosphere, then one would expect them to remain permanently in the earth's crust and one could detect them by measuring their charges in a modified Millikan apparatus. The considerations involved are complex since we know very little about the chemistry of quarks and it is not possible to do much more than guess where they would become most concentrated. However, the evidence is that there is less than one quark per 10^{20} nucleons in ordinary matter.

Finally, several experiments have looked for a flux of quarks in cosmic radiation. Most of these experiments have been unsuccessful. However, the Sydney group (McCusker and Cairns 1969, Cairns et al. 1969) have reported evidence for fractionally charged particles in the extensive air showers produced by primary cosmic ray particles of energy greater than 10^6 GeV. Their work has been widely discussed, but it is not yet generally accepted that the observed phenomena are produced by fractionally charged particles. All three types of search involve rather complicated questions and the reader is referred to the articles by Massam (1968), and Király and Wolfendale (1970) for references and more detailed discussions. It is, however, quite clear that quarks, if they exist at all, are produced in much smaller quantities in all the reactions examined than one would expect from experience with other hadrons. This does not rule out the possibility that they exist, but it does mean that present evidence gives very little encouragement for the extreme quark hypothesis.

Three main hypotheses have been advanced to explain why quarks could exist despite the unsuccessful searches. First, it has been suggested that they might be very heavy. Present accelerators would then have insufficient energy to produce them. Moreover, for known particles the production cross section falls very rapidly with increasing particle mass and it could be that quarks are so massive that neither existing nor planned accelerators will have sufficient *intensity* to produce them. (See for example the discussion by Massam 1968.) If particles with integral charge are physically composed of quarks, then the binding energy must be so large that it is difficult to see how it can be due to the strong interaction alone. It may be that an SU_3-conserving *super-strong* interaction binds the quarks, but there is at present no evidence for this hypothesis. It would indeed be unsatisfactory to find that, having invented quarks to explain the systematics of the strong interaction, one had then to postulate that the quarks themselves were bound by a different interaction. Secondly, it has been pointed out that quarks might not be very massive, but that their production might be inhibited by some as yet unknown dynamical factor. Finally, it is possible that quarks exist within integrally charged particles, but that charge quantization somehow prevents one from observing individual quarks widely separated. This would mean that certain interaction phenomena could be explained in terms of quark–quark interactions, rather as certain phenomena are now explained in terms of exchange of virtual particles, but that isolated quarks could never be observed. Some evidence for this has been reported but it is not yet convincing.

To sum up, there are four possibilities for the status of real quarks. First and most likely is that they do not exist. In this case, SU_3 on its own would give an incomplete account of particle systematics. Additional requirements, including SU_2 and charge quantization, would be needed to specify which particles actually exist. Secondly, it may be that particles with non-integral charge exist but that the familiar particles are not composed of them. There could be many reasons why they have not been observed. The most likely is that they are very massive. Present evidence is entirely consistent with this hypothesis, but of course offers no support for it. Thirdly, it may be that in some sense quarks exist within observed particles, but that they can never be isolated. They could then be used in an explanatory model, but would not otherwise be particularly interesting. Finally, it may be that existing particles are physically composed of quarks and that they will eventually be isolated. This is a very strong and far reaching hypothesis. Several difficulties are attached to it, but they are not sufficient finally to disprove it. However, the long succession of unsuccessful quark searches has been discouraging, and powerful positive evidence will be required before it can be taken very seriously. We emphasize that the discovery of particles with fractional charges would not on its own prove the extreme quark hypothesis. It is perfectly possible that such particles exist, but that the more familiar particles are not composed of them. A long and very detailed set of experiments would be needed and it seems fair to say that there is little chance that such a set will be completed within the next few years. In what follows, we show explicitly how elementary triplets could be used to construct observed SU_3 multiplets. However, we take the view that the existence of quarks is very problematical, and so make little use of them. They are discussed more fully by Feld (1967).

5.4. Direct products and interactions

In this section, we consider some related topics, all involving the reduction of SU_3 tensors. We have already seen something of the value of a classification scheme based on irreducible multiplets. The properties of the elements of these multiplets can be divided into two classes: the operators corresponding to the first class can be expressed in terms of SU_3 generators and their eigenvalues can be calculated using SU_3 algebra; most of the properties of the second class are common to all elements of the multiplet. There are a few exceptions which arise from the fact that SU_3 is not an exact symmetry. These are discussed in Sections 5.6, 5.7. We next consider how to combine multiplets by taking direct products, and how to reduce these direct products to new multiplets. The treatment follows closely the one used for SU_2. First we consider the construction of low ranking multiplets out of elementary triplets or quarks. This gives the theoretical basis for the rules of the quark model. Then we consider direct products more generally and give two rules for reducing them. One is an extension of the methods derived for SU_2. The other is new. It is not justified, but is presented as a simple and extremely useful rule of thumb. Many of the questions discussed have been raised in general terms in earlier sections, but some specific examples should be helpful.

Consider the quark–anti-quark system. This must necessarily have zero baryon number and hence any observed particles would be mesons. The system can be written as a general tensor, A, with elements

$$A^p_j \equiv V_j V^p, \tag{5.36}$$

where j, p can each run from one to three. There are thus nine independent states and we require suitable linear combinations of these so that A can be divided into irreducible multiplets. Now this problem has already been considered in Section 5.2, and we have seen that the general nonet can be divided into a scalar singlet and a traceless octet. This is conveniently summarized as

$$3 \times \bar{3} = 8 + 1. \tag{5.37}$$

On this model, one would expect the lightest meson states to be members of singlets or octets. Larger multiplets would have to contain more quarks. At present, there is no convincing evidence that we need to go beyond a simple quark–anti-quark system. But we shall see later that the classification into singlet and octet states is not quite as trivial as the present treatment suggests.

Next consider the two quark system. If individual quarks have baryon number $\frac{1}{3}$, then this system has baryon number $\frac{2}{3}$ and cannot correspond to any states which have been observed so far. It can be written as a general tensor, A, with elements

$$A_{jk} \equiv V_j V_k. \tag{5.38}$$

Since j, k can each run from one to three, A can be reduced. Consider a new tensor, B, with elements

$$B^l \equiv \epsilon^{jkl} A_{jk}. \tag{5.39}$$

B has three non-zero elements and is thus a covariant triplet.

$$B^1 = (\sqrt{\tfrac{1}{2}})(A_{23} - A_{32}), \qquad B^2 = (\sqrt{\tfrac{1}{2}})(A_{31} - A_{13}),$$

$$B_3 = (\sqrt{\tfrac{1}{2}})(A_{12} - A_{21}). \tag{5.40}$$

The remaining six linearly independent states are totally symmetric in their lower indices and thus form an irreducible sextet with elements

$$A_{11}, \qquad A_{22}, \qquad A_{33}, \qquad (\sqrt{\tfrac{1}{2}})(A_{23} + A_{32}),$$

$$(\sqrt{\tfrac{1}{2}})(A_{31} + A_{13}), \qquad (\sqrt{\tfrac{1}{2}})(A_{12} + A_{21}). \tag{5.41}$$

Thus the general covariant nonet can be reduced to a contravariant

triplet and a covariant sextet. This reduction is conveniently summarized in the schematic form

$$3 \times 3 = \bar{3} + 6. \tag{5.42}$$

We remarked earlier that, if particles with fractional charge exist
and charge is conserved, then at least one state with charge $(m + \frac{1}{3})e$
and one with charge $(m + \frac{2}{3})e$, where m is an integer and e is the electronic
charge, must be completely stable against decay. Assuming that one
quark and one anti-quark are stable, then the stability of a bound two-
quark system can be deduced using familiar reasoning. The most
energetically favourable decay channel would be to a baryon and an
anti-quark. If such a channel exists, with mass less than the mass of the
two-quark system, and with other quantum numbers correct, then the
decay will occur. Otherwise, a bound two-quark system composed of the
lightest quarks will be stable. In particular, if quarks are lighter than
nucleons, then the bound two-quark system will always be stable.
Similarly, it is quite possible that a whole family of stable bound multi-
quark states may exist in analogy to the known stable multi-nucleon
states.

Now consider a three-quark system. In the last section, we required
that this should have unit baryon number and so the corresponding
observed particles would be baryons. In order to do this, we had to
postulate that quarks have baryon number $\frac{1}{3}$. This postulate is justified
only if the three-quark system can include all the lightest observed
baryon multiplets. The next step is to show that it can. Let us use eqn
(5.42) to define the elements of a three-quark tensor, A, as

$$A_{jkl} \equiv V_j V_k V_l \equiv (B^p + C_{jk}) V_l, \tag{5.43}$$

where eqn (5.43) defines two new tensors, B, C. B is a contravariant
triplet and C is a covariant sextet. Next, using eqn (5.37), we can
decompose

$$BV \equiv D + S, \tag{5.44}$$

where D is an irreducible octet and S is a singlet. Now consider the
elements $C_{jk} V_l$. We can separate out the antisymmetric part as a
tensor, E, with elements

$$E_k^m \equiv \epsilon^{jlm} C_{jk} V_l. \tag{5.45}$$

Now k, m can each run from one to three and so at first sight E is an
unreduced mixed rank-two tensor with nine elements. However, on

attempting to take its trace we find

$$\delta^k_m E^m_k = \delta^k_m \epsilon^{jlm} C_{jk} V_l = -\epsilon^{jml} C_{jm} V_l = 0, \qquad (5.46)$$

since C is totally symmetric. Thus E is traceless and is, in fact, an irreducible octet. We can therefore decompose

$$CV = E + F. \qquad (5.47)$$

But, by construction

$$\epsilon^{jkl} F_{jkl} = 0 \qquad (5.48)$$

F is totally symmetric in its three lower indices and is an irreducible decuplet. Eqns (5.43), (5.44), (5.47) may be summarized schematically as

$$3 \times 3 \times 3 = 1 + 8 + 8 + 10. \qquad (5.49)$$

On this model, one would expect the lightest baryon states to be singlets, octets and decuplets. This is precisely what is observed and this fact forms the justification for assigning to quarks a baryon number $\frac{1}{3}$. At present there is no clear evidence for the existence of mesons belonging to larger multiplets than the singlet and octet, or for baryons belonging to larger multiplets than the singlet, octet, and decuplet. It is thus convenient, at least as a model, to consider mesons as quark–anti-quark systems, and baryons as three-quark systems. Members of higher rank multiplets are called 'exotic states'. Some of these states could easily be recognized by their unusual quantum numbers. For instance, a meson with isospin 2 or a baryon with hypercharge $+2$ would be exotic. Vigorous searches are being made for such states. These searches have not been successful, but it is too early to say whether this is because such states simply happen to be heavy or difficult to detect, or whether we should look for some more fundamental and far-reaching explanation. This completes the discussion of multi-quark states and the physical basis for the quark model. We next consider multi-particle states from a more general standpoint.

When two particles interact, the resultant state may be described by an element of the tensor which is the direct product of the tensors containing the two interacting particles. The new tensors produced can be determined by reducing this direct product in the usual way. The relative probabilities with which the various possible tensor elements are produced depends on the SU_3 Clebsch–Gordan coefficients. These are necessarily more complicated than the SU_2 coefficients in the general case. However, we shall see in the next section that there are many special cases for which they can readily be expressed in terms of the

SU_2 coefficients. Assuming SU_3 invariance, the strong interaction is an SU_3 scalar and so all SU_3 quantum numbers are conserved. The cross section for the two-particle reaction can be expressed in terms of a reduced matrix element, which depends on which irreducible *tensor* is formed but not on which *tensor element*. The only other factors which appear are the SU_3 Clebsch–Gordan coefficients. These rules are analogous to the isospin rules given in Section 4.5. For the rest of this section, we shall discuss the reduction of direct products of irreducible tensors. In the following section we shall consider certain properties of the SU_3 Clebsch–Gordan coefficients.

The standard method for reduction can be illustrated using an important special case. Let B, C be two irreducible octets and let A be their direct product. Then the elements of A are given by

$$A_{jk}^{pq} \equiv B_j^p C_k^q. \tag{5.50}$$

We require to separate the elements of A into groups of independent linear combinations such that each group is irreducible. First, decompose A into a symmetric and an antisymmetric part.

$$A_{jk}^{pq} = \tfrac{1}{2}(A_{jk}^{pq} + A_{jk}^{qp}) + \tfrac{1}{2}(A_{jk}^{pq} - A_{jk}^{qp}) \equiv D_{jk}^{pq} + F_{jk}^{pq} \tag{5.51}$$

where eqn (5.51) defines the tensors D, F. Now D includes a singlet

$$S \equiv \delta_p^k \delta_p^j D_{jk}^{pq}, \tag{5.52}$$

and an octet, E, with elements

$$E_j^q = \delta_p^k D_{jk}^{pq}. \tag{5.53}$$

(Since we have already separated out the singlet, S, the trace of E is zero.) At first sight, one might hope to separate out a second octet using δ_p^j. However, it is easy to see by comparison with eqn (5.51) that this is in fact the *same* octet as E. Thus

$$D = S + E + G, \tag{5.54}$$

where G is a mixed rank four tensor with elements G_{jk}^{pq}. Since G contains those linear combinations of the elements of D which are left when all traces have been extracted, it follows that its traces must all be zero. Hence, if G is symmetric in both upper and lower indices, then it is irreducible. But it is easy to see that it *is* symmetric in both upper and lower indices by the following argument. First note that, by definition, it is symmetric under permutation of *both* upper and lower indices. Hence any part which is antisymmetric in the upper indices is also antisymmetric in the lower indices. Let us extract this part. We define a new mixed rank-two tensor, H, with elements

$$
\begin{aligned}
H^l_r &\equiv \epsilon_{pqr}\epsilon^{jkl}G^{pq}_{jk} \\
&= (\delta^j_p\delta^k_q\delta^l_r + \delta^k_p\delta^l_q\delta^j_r + \delta^l_p\delta^j_q\delta^k_r - \delta^l_p\delta^k_p\delta^j_r - \delta^k_q\delta^j_q\delta^l_r - \\
&\quad - \delta^j_p\delta^l_q\delta^k_r)G^{pq}_{jk} \\
&= 0,
\end{aligned}
\tag{5.55}
$$

since all traces are zero. It follows that G is totally symmetric and hence irreducible. It is, in fact, a 27-plet (cf. eqn 5.10). The notation used here gives a convenient way to keep track of the indices. However, one should remember that eqns (5.52), (5.53) are simply a short way to write linear combinations of the elements of A. They could if necessary be expanded as we expanded the elements of the irreducible octet explicitly in Section 5.2 (cf. eqns (5.23), (5.25)). This task has been left as an exercise for the reader.

Next, consider the reduction of the antisymmetric tensor, F. It contains no singlet since

$$
\delta^k_p\delta^j_q F^{pq}_{jk} = 0,
\tag{5.56}
$$

but we can extract an octet, K, with elements

$$
K^q_j = \delta^k_p F^{pq}_{jk}.
\tag{5.57}
$$

As before, the remainder has all traces zero. It is anti-symmetric under permutation of both upper and lower indices. Hence any part which is antisymmetric in the upper indices is symmetric in the lower indices. Let us therefore define a new tensor, L, with elements

$$
L_{jkl} \equiv \epsilon_{pql} F^{pq}_{jk}.
\tag{5.58}
$$

Using the same expansion as in eqn (5.55), one can show that L is totally symmetric. It is a decuplet. Similarly, the part of F which is symmetric in the upper indices is antisymmetric in the lower indices and forms the $\overline{10}$. The reduction is now complete and may be summarized schematically as

$$
8 \times 8 = 1 + 8 + 8 + 10 + \overline{10} + 27.
\tag{5.59}
$$

Note that there are two octets—the symmetric one, eqn (5.53), known as the 'D-coupling octet' and the antisymmetric one, eqn (5.57), known as the 'F-coupling octet'. Note also that the total number of linearly independent elements is left unchanged by the reduction. The sum of the multiplicities on the right hand side is equal to the product of the multiplicities on the left hand side.

Clearly, we could use this rather simple-minded method to reduce the direct products of larger multiplets, but equally clearly the argument could become very complicated indeed. Fortunately there is an admirable theorem, due to Speiser (1964), which makes the labour unnecessary. We state the theorem, but omit the proof which is far from trivial. Consider Fig. 5.7. Multiplets are denoted by their multiplicity.

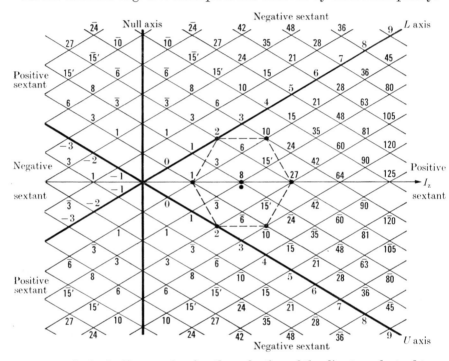

FIG. 5.7. Speiser's diagram showing the reduction of the direct product of two octets.

They occupy the points on the lattice given by their values of L, U. Thus the octet lies on the point $L = U = 1$ and the decuplet lies on the point $L = 3$, $U = 0$. (Note that the zero lines are one unit away from the axes. The points on the axes do not correspond to multiplets.) To find the direct product of two multiplets, B, C say, superimpose the weight diagram for B on the Speiser diagram, with its origin ($Y = I_z = 0$) on the point corresponding to C. Now whenever an element of the weight diagram for B coincides with a lattice point, then the multiplet at the lattice point appears in the reduction of the direct product, with positive or negative sign depending on the sextant, and with multiplicity equal to the number of elements at that point in the weight diagram.

The example shown in Fig. 5.7 is the reduction of the direct product of two octets. The weight diagram for the octet was given in Fig. 5.1. It has two elements at the origin and one at every other point. This diagram is now superimposed on the lattice with its origin at the point corresponding to the octet ($L = U = 1$). Two of the elements lie on the axes and so do not correspond to new multiplets. The remaining six elements correspond to the six multiplets given in eqn (5.59). In this example, all points lie in a positive sextant. Suppose, however, that the decuplet (Fig. 5.3) had been superimposed on the point corresponding to the octet. Then Speiser's method would give the decomposition

$$8 \times 10 = -1 + 10 + 35 + 1 + 8 + 27 + \overline{10} - \overline{10} = 8 + 10 + 27 + 35. \quad (5.60)$$

The reader should verify that the same result is obtained by superimposing the weight diagram for the octet on the point corresponding to the decuplet. Note once again that the sum of the multiplicities on the right hand side is equal to the product of the multiplicities on the left hand side.

Speiser's method does not tell us how to write the elements of the reduced tensors in terms of the elements of the original tensors. In order to do this, the more direct method must be used. However, Speiser's method is an extremely useful rule of thumb and the reader should amuse himself by showing that it yields eqns (5.36), (5.42), (5.49).

5.5. I, U and V spins

When discussing the reduction of direct products, we have so far considered which multiplets can be formed, but not their relative probabilities. That is, we have not derived the SU_3 Clebsch–Gordan coefficients. The latter problem has been discussed by de Swart (1963) and some of the coefficients have been tabulated by McNamee and Chilton (1964). However, it turns out that for most practical purposes this full treatment is unnecessary. Most of the results can in fact be derived using the familiar SU_2 Clebsch–Gordan coefficients and we shall therefore simply discuss how this is done.

We start by remembering that SU_2 is in a sense contained within SU_3. Values of the third component of isospin can be determined for any element of an SU_3 multiplet using eqn (5.11). Further, when L, U, λ, λ' are fixed the permitted states can be grouped to form an isospin multiplet, with I given by eqn (5.34). Strictly speaking, pure SU_3 does not require that we should do this. It allows us to place states on a plot of Y against I_z, but if there is more than one element at any point on the plot, then there will be SU_3 degeneracy, and we have to invoke SU_2 in order to decide which linear combinations of tensor elements correspond to physical states. An example of this was given in Section 5.2 when we considered the octet. In practice, this introduces no difficulty since SU_2 is an exact symmetry of the strong interaction.

When states have been grouped into isospin multiplets, we can write down how the interactions between members of two multiplets are related using the simple SU_2 Clebsch–Gordan coefficients. The more complicated SU_3 coefficients, of course, give the same results in this special case. However, this is not the only set of SU_3 coefficients which can be obtained using SU_2. We could obtain another set of SU_2 transformations by keeping L, U, p, p' fixed and allowing only n, n', λ, λ' to vary. The generators of these transformations, by analogy with the I_x, I_y, I_z defined by eqn (5.3), would be

$$U_x = \tfrac{1}{2}\lambda_6, \qquad U_y = \tfrac{1}{2}\lambda_7, \qquad U_z = \tfrac{1}{4}(\sqrt{3}\lambda_8 - \lambda_3), \qquad (5.61)$$

where the definition of U_z is chosen to give

$$U_z = \tfrac{1}{2}\begin{pmatrix} 0 & 0 & 0 \\ 0 & 1 & 0 \\ 0 & 0 & -1 \end{pmatrix}. \qquad (5.62)$$

It is diagonal and hence all SU_3 states are eigenstates. By comparison with eqns (5.3), (5.5), the definition (5.61) gives

$$U_z = \tfrac{3}{4}Y - \tfrac{1}{2}I_z. \qquad (5.63)$$

Thus the U_z quantum number can be expressed immediately in terms of the isospin and hypercharge quantum numbers. Alternatively, using eqn (4.85) it can be deduced from the SU_3 tensor indices.

$$[U_zA](\mu) = \tfrac{1}{2}(n - \lambda - n' + \lambda')A(\mu). \qquad (5.64)$$

The three generators define a new SU_2 space called U-spin space which is also, in a sense, contained within SU_3. Once again, it is possible to take linear combinations of the SU_3 elements and form U-spin multiplets. Now since U_x, U_y, U_z all commute with the charge operator, Q, given by eqn (5.6), all members of a U-spin multiplet have the same charge. If we make the natural further assumption that all their other electromagnetic properties are the same, then the electromagnetic interaction will not distinguish between them. In what follows, we shall explore the physical consequences of this postulate. It turns out that they hold very well in practice. The postulate implies that U-spin is an exact symmetry of the electromagnetic interaction, just as isospin is an exact symmetry of the strong interaction. Many of the results which we have derived for the one also apply to the other, but there is an important difference. We have remarked that, although SU_3 elements can be grouped in linear combinations to form isospin multiplets, strictly speaking SU_3 itself does not require us to do this. It is the *additional* requirement that isospin should be an exact symmetry of the strong interaction, which means that, since physical states are strong interaction eigenstates, they must also be isospin eigenstates. But U-spin is *not* an exact symmetry of the strong interaction. This can easily be seen by noticing that U^2 does not commute with the generators, I_x, I_y, I_z of isospin. It follows that physical states are not necessarily U-spin eigenstates. We can see the implications of this by noticing that U_x, U_y, U_z can be obtained from I_x, I_y, I_z by a simple permutation of rows and columns. Hence the eigenvalues of U^2 are given by an equation exactly analogous to eqn (5.16), but with n, λ, p substituted for p, n, λ respectively. Clearly, by analogy with eqns (5.17), (5.18), if a state tensor has lower indices only, then all its elements are U-spin eigenstates with

$$[U^2 A](\mu) = \tfrac{1}{4}(n + \lambda)(n + \lambda + 2)A(\mu), \qquad (5.65)$$

and if it has upper indices only, then

$$[U^2 A](\mu) = \tfrac{1}{4}(n' + \lambda')(n' + \lambda' + 2)A(\mu). \qquad (5.66)$$

But if it has both upper and lower indices then not every state which is consistent with SU_3 is necessarily an eigenstate of U^2. It is always possible to group SU_3 elements into U-spin eigenstates, but this time there is no guarantee that such eigenstates exist physically. The most that we can say is that all physical states can be expressed as linear combinations of U-spin eigenstates and vice versa.

Perhaps an example may help to make this clear. In Section 5.2, we considered the octet and found that six points on its weight diagram were each occupied by only a single element. They are therefore isospin and U-spin eigenstates. However the seventh (central) point was occupied by two elements and these two elements were SU_3 degenerate.

Now, eqns (5.23), (5.25) show how to combine them into isospin eigenstates.

$$I = 1, \qquad (\sqrt{\tfrac{1}{2}})(A_1^1 - A_2^2); \tag{5.67}$$

$$I = 0, \qquad (\sqrt{\tfrac{1}{6}})(A_1^1 + A_2^2 - 2A_3^3). \tag{5.68}$$

For the $J^P = \tfrac{1}{2}^+$ baryon octet, these would represent the state Σ^0, Λ^0 respectively. Now the corresponding pure U-spin eigenstate may be obtained by noticing that, in U-spin algebra, the index 2 play the part played by the index 1 in isospin algebra. Similarly, 3 plays the part of 2 and 1 plays the part of 3. Hence the pure U-spin states with $U_z = Q = 0$ are

$$U = 1, \qquad (\sqrt{\tfrac{1}{2}})(A_2^2 - A_3^3) \equiv \Sigma_U{}^0, \qquad \text{say;} \tag{5.69}$$

$$U = 0, \qquad (\sqrt{\tfrac{1}{6}})(A_2^2 + A_3^3 - 2A_1^1) \equiv \Lambda_U{}^0, \qquad \text{say.} \tag{5.70}$$

These two states are not isospin eigenstates, but they may readily be expressed in terms of isospin eigenstates.

$$\Sigma_U{}^0 = \frac{\sqrt{3}}{2}\Lambda^0 - \tfrac{1}{2}\Sigma^0, \qquad \Lambda_U{}^0 = -\tfrac{1}{2}\Lambda^0 - \frac{\sqrt{3}}{2}\Sigma^0. \tag{5.71}$$

Similarly, all other U-spin eigenstates can be expressed in terms of physical states.

Now, if U-spin is an exact symmetry of the electromagnetic inter action, we can immediately make a number of predictions by analogy with the predictions about the strong interaction which were listed in Section 4.5. When two particles interact electromagnetically, the resultant may be described by an element of the U-spin tensor which is the direct product of the tensors containing the two interacting particles. The resultant tensor may be reduced in the usual way, and the relative amplitudes of the different U-spin states can be deduced using the SU_2 Clebsch–Gordan coefficients. Similarly, in an electromagnetic interaction, both total U-spin and its third component are conserved. Finally, one can express reaction cross sections in terms of reduced matrix elements which depend on total U-spin, but not on its third component. The only other factors are the usual SU_2 Clebsch–Gordan coefficients but this time, of course, states must be described in terms of their U-spin quantum numbers and not their isospin quantum numbers. All the algebra is exactly the same as for isospin.

Finally, one can define a third SU_2 space, called V-spin space, by keeping L, U, n, n' fixed and allowing p, p', λ, λ' to vary. This is no quite so useful since it is not an exact symmetry of either the strong or the electromagnetic interaction. Nevertheless, it is approximately conserved and so can give a further set of relations.

The weight diagram provides a useful method for displaying the I, U, V quantum numbers. The U- and V-spin axes lie at $120°$ to each other and to the isospin axis. The $J^P = \frac{1}{2}^+$ baryon octet, for instance, is shown in Fig. 5.8. By inspection, the proton and Σ^+ form a U-spin

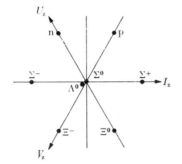

Fig. 5.8. Weight diagram for the $J^P = \frac{1}{2}^+$ baryon octet showing the I, U, V axes.

doublet. Their total U-spin is $\frac{1}{2}$. The third components are $+\frac{1}{2}$, $-\frac{1}{2}$ for p, Σ^+ respectively. Similarly, the quantum numbers of all other pure U-spin states can be deduced by inspection.

5.6. SU_3 mass formulae

The last section completed the account of the particle properties which can be predicted assuming that SU_3 is an exact symmetry. We have already remarked that there are various properties for which this assumption must be relaxed, but that interesting results can be derived using first-order perturbation theory. In the present section, we apply first-order perturbation theory to the SU_3 mass formulae. We follow the strategy outlined at the beginning of the chapter. Assumptions are introduced one by one and their consequences checked against experimental observations. Most of these assumptions are manifestly first order approximations and the predictions made using them can be expected to hold only roughly. Some, however, might be expected to hold to higher order and here we find that the predictions are very accurate. Throughout the section it is important to be clear which assumptions are being used and how accurate they are likely to be. It turns out that baryon and meson masses must be treated in a slightly different way. The formulae for baryon masses can be derived using simple and rather natural assumptions. The formulae for meson masses are somewhat more surprising and the physical explanation more *ad hoc*. Nevertheless, they give useful information about symmetry breaking and hence much insight into the essential logic of SU_3. In the following section, we apply the same ideas to electromagnetic properties.

The treatment of SU_2 assumed that isospin is an exact symmetry for the strong interaction but not for the electromagnetic interaction. All mass differences between members of isospin multiplets were therefore ascribed to electromagnetic effects. So far, we have made the same assumption about SU_3. Now, if this were correct, all members of an SU_3 multiplet would have the same mass except for relatively small electromagnetic splitting. However, a glance at the standard mass tables shows that this is not the case. The mass splittings within typical SU_3 multiplets are of the order of hundreds of MeV, compared with typically less than 10 MeV for the electromagnetic mass splittings within isospin multiplets. We are thus forced to conclude that SU_3 is *not* an exact symmetry of the strong interaction. The present section deals with some of the consequences of this conclusion.

Now of course the success of SU_3 as a classification scheme means that it is at least approximately true. We shall therefore consider the strong interaction to be composed of the strong interaction proper, *defined* as being SU_3 invariant, plus a *semi-strong* interaction which is SU_3 breaking. We shall calculate the properties of this semi-strong interaction using first-order perturbation theory. Consider the mass operator. In its most general form it is an SU_3 tensor and can therefore be written as the sum of elements of irreducible tensors. The strong interaction part of this mass operator satisfies SU_3 exactly, and therefore produces no splitting within a multiplet. It has the same eigenvalue for all elements of the multiplet, and it follows that it must commute with all the generators, λ_j, of SU_3. It is therefore an SU_3 scalar.

Now consider the semi-strong part of the mass operator. By definition, it produces mass splitting and therefore cannot be an SU_3 scalar. However, since SU_2 is a good symmetry for the strong interaction, it cannot produce any mass splitting within an isospin multiplet, and must therefore commute with all the generators, $\lambda_1, \lambda_2, \lambda_3$ of isospin. And since hypercharge is a good quantum number in strong interactions it must commute with that too. These are powerful restrictions. The semi-strong mass operator must have zero matrix elements between states of different isospin or different hypercharge. Thus, if it is an element of an irreducible SU_3 tensor operator, it must be the element with $I = Y = 0$. By eqn (5.1), charge must be zero also. Hence using eqns (5.11–13),

$$p - p' = n - n' = \lambda - \lambda' = 0, \tag{5.72}$$

$$L = U. \tag{5.73}$$

The mass splitting operator must be a linear combination of the $I = Y = 0$ elements of the tensor operators with $L = U = 0, 1, 2, \ldots$. The simplest approximation is to retain only the first two terms: those from the singlet and the octet. The singlet is the SU_3 scalar already discussed and hence the semi-strong part of the mass operator is an octet element of the form given by eqn (5.25):

$$M = (\sqrt{\tfrac{1}{6}})(A_1^1 + A_2^2 - 2A_3^3), \tag{5.74}$$

where the A_j^i are all, of course, operators. Clearly at this stage we have made two major approximations. We have assumed that mass splitting can be calculated using first order perturbation theory, and we have assumed that the mass operator is an element of an octet. These assumptions are plausible, but justified only if they give the right answer. It turns out that they are remarkably successful.

Now so far the only restriction on M is that it should have the form (5.74). Since it represents an observable, it must be linear in the matrix and vector formalism used in Chapter 1. If it were also linear in SU_3 then it follows from eqn (5.74) that it could be written as the SU_3 matrix

$$M = \frac{c}{\sqrt{6}} \begin{pmatrix} 1 & 0 & 0 \\ 0 & 1 & 0 \\ 0 & 0 & -2 \end{pmatrix}, \tag{5.75}$$

where c is a real constant. Comparison with eqn (5.4) shows that M would then be proportional to the hypercharge operator. Thus any mass splitting produced by a linear operator must be directly proportional to hypercharge. Unfortunately, there is no reason at all to conclude that M should be linear in the tensor formalism of SU_3. Mass is not one of those operators like charge or hypercharge which can be expressed directly as a linear combination of the SU_3 generators. Moveover when physical states are expressed in the compressed tensor notation, it is not possible to represent every hermitian operator within the restricted framework of 3×3 matrices. The operator for total isospin is an obvious case in point. It is expressed as a linear combination of the *squares* of λ_1, λ_2, λ_3 (cf. eqns (4.16), (5.3)). We are therefore

11*

driven to ask what is the most general form that M can take. We know that its expectation value must be a scalar and so must be obtained by taking some scalar linear combination, $\langle A|M|A \rangle$, of the elements

$$A^{*p'q'...t'}_{j'k'...m'} M^{\alpha'}_{\alpha} A^{jk...m}_{pq...t}.$$ (5.76)

The technique for taking scalar linear combinations was outlined in Section 4.4. Either the δ or the ϵ tensors can be used. However, (5.76) has an equal number of upper and lower indices and so, if the covariant ϵ tensor is used, the contravariant tensor must be used also. Now, the discussion of eqn (5.55) showed that the product of covariant and contravariant ϵ tensors can always be expressed in terms of the δ tensors. We therefore confine our attention to these alone. Since A, M are both irreducible, all their traces must be zero and there are only two logically distinct ways to make the contraction.

$$A^{*\alpha q...t}_{jk...m} M^{\alpha'}_{\alpha} A^{jk...m}_{\alpha' q...t} \equiv M_1,$$ (5.77)

$$A^{*pq...t}_{\alpha' k...m} M^{\alpha}_{\alpha} A^{\alpha k...m}_{pq...t} \equiv M_2,$$ (5 78)

where eqns (5.77), (5.78) define M_1, M_2 respectively. Consider the consequences of these equations for the three multiplets discussed in Section 5.2.

1. *The singlet, S.* M_1, M_2 both go to zero. There is thus (of course) no mass splitting in the singlet.

2. *The octet,* with elements A^p_j. Comparing eqns (5.75), (5.77), (5.78) and using the notation of Section 5.1,

$$M_1 = \frac{c_1}{\sqrt{6}}(p+n-2\lambda), \qquad M_2 = \frac{c_2}{\sqrt{6}}(p'+n'-2\lambda')$$ (5.79)

where c_1, c_2 are real constants. Let us write the mass of an isospin multiplet with isospin, I, and hypercharge, Y, as $M_{(I,Y)}$. Then the masses of three out of the four isospin multiplets, (5.26), are given immediately.

$$M_{(\frac{1}{2},1)} = \sqrt{\tfrac{1}{6}}(c_1-2c_2)+M_0, \qquad M_{(1,0)} = \sqrt{\tfrac{1}{6}}(c_1+c_2)+M_0,$$

$$M_{(\frac{1}{2},-1)} = \sqrt{\tfrac{1}{6}}(-2c_1+c_2)+M_0,$$ (5.80)

where M_0 is the eigenvalue of the scalar mass operator which arises from the strong interaction proper. The expectation values of M_1, M_2 for the isospin singlet may be evaluated directly to give

$$M_{(0,0)} = \sqrt{\tfrac{1}{6}}(-c_1-c_2)+M_0.$$ (5.81)

Eliminating M_0, c_1, c_2 between eqns (5.80), (5.81) gives

$$2M_{(\frac{1}{2},1)} + 2M_{(\frac{1}{2},-1)} = 3M_{(0,0)} + M_{(1,0)}. \qquad (5.82)$$

This is the celebrated Gell-Mann–Okubo mass formula for the octet. We have derived it using first-order perturbation theory, and assuming that the mass splitting operator is an element of an irreducible octet. The reader will find that it has been proved in the literature by several methods, most of them perfectly plausible. When examining the proofs, however, it is important to look beyond the formalism to the actual physical assumptions which are being made.

3. *The decuplet* with elements A_{jkl}. In this case, M_1 is directly proportional to the hypercharge and M_2 is zero. Hence the masses of the elements vary linearly with their hypercharge.

These results have been generalized by Gell-Mann and Okubo (1962) who have shown that the mass operator has eigenvalues of the form

$$M = M_a + M_b Y + M_c \{I(I+1) - \tfrac{1}{4}Y^2\}, \qquad (5.83)$$

where M_a, M_b, M_c are constants. This can be proved by evaluating M_1, M_2 in the general case. (See, for instance, Van Hove 1965.) It is easy to check that eqn (5.83) yields our results for the singlet, octet and decuplet as special cases.

We have remarked that the assumptions used to obtain these results are plausible but justified only if they give the right answers. We shall therefore check them using some special cases. First consider the $J^P = \frac{1}{2}^+$ baryon octet shown in Fig. 5.2. It contains four isospin multiplets—nucleon, Σ, Λ, Ξ. Eqn (5.82) yields

$$2M_N + 2M_\Xi = 3M_\Lambda + M_\Sigma \qquad (5.84)$$

Substituting mean masses from the tables (Rittenberg *et al.* 1971) gives

$$\text{LHS} = 4513\cdot8 \pm 0\cdot7 \text{ MeV}, \qquad \text{RHS} = 4539\cdot9 \pm 0\cdot2 \text{ MeV}. \quad (5.85)$$

The discrepancy is only about 7 MeV per particle which is of the same order as the mass splitting within isospin multiplets. Eqn (5.84) seems to be correct up to terms of the size of electromagnetic mass splitting.

Next consider the $J^P = \frac{3}{2}^+$ decuplet shown in Fig. 5.4. Here the masses should depend linearly on hypercharge. The actual masses are

$$\begin{array}{ll} M_{N^*} = 1233 \ \pm \ 3\text{ MeV} & M_{Y^*} = 1384\cdot5 \pm 1\cdot5\text{ MeV} \\[2mm] M_{\Xi^*} = 1531\cdot4 \pm 1\cdot5\text{ MeV} & M_\Omega = 1672\cdot5 \pm 0\cdot5\text{ MeV} \end{array} \qquad (5.86)$$

with differences $141 \cdot 1 \pm 1 \cdot 6$, $146 \cdot 9 \pm 2 \cdot 1$, $151 \cdot 5 \pm 3$ MeV. Thus once again the prediction is very well confirmed.

Now consider the $J^P = 0^-$ meson octet shown in Fig. (5.2). It contains four isospin multiplets—K, π, η, $\bar{K}$—with mean masses

$$M_K = M_{\bar{K}} = 495 \cdot 8 \pm 0 \cdot 1 \text{ MeV} \qquad M_\pi = 138 \cdot 04 \pm 0 \cdot 01 \text{ MeV}$$
$$M_\eta = 548 \cdot 8 \pm 0 \cdot 6 \text{ MeV}. \tag{5.87}$$

Since K, $\bar{K}$ are charge conjugate states, they have the same mass and eqn (5.82) reduces to

$$4M_K = 3M_\eta + M_\pi. \tag{5.88}$$

Substituting the mass values given by eqns (5.87)

$$\text{LHS} = 1983 \cdot 2 \pm 0 \cdot 4 \text{ MeV.} \qquad \text{RHS} = 1784 \cdot 4 \pm 1 \cdot 8 \text{ MeV.} \tag{5.89}$$

Eqn (5.88) is thus very badly satisfied and it follows that at least one of our assumptions has broken down. Since eqn (5.88) is the only explicit prediction for the 0^- octet, a variety of *ad hoc* hypotheses could be introduced to make theory and experiment agree. However, the success of the approach when applied to baryon masses means that it is desirable to make as small a change as possible. Thus, one would like to retain the hypothesis that the mass operator is an octet element of the form (5·74), and, if possible, one would like to continue using first-order perturbation theory. Since the meson mass splitting is relatively very much larger than the baryon mass splitting, the latter assumption becomes somewhat less plausible. However, it is reasonable to argue that the discrepancy in eqn (5.89) is too large to be explained simply by second-order effects. The clue is to notice that strictly speaking all we known about M is that it is a *mass* operator. Its eigenvalue may in fact be *any* function of mass. It has therefore been suggested that for bosons we should interpret it as giving the *squares* of the physical masses. In that case

$$\text{LHS} = 0 \cdot 983 \text{ (GeV)}^2, \qquad \text{RHS} = 0 \cdot 923 \text{ (GeV)}^2. \tag{5.90}$$

The discrepancy is now small enough to be explained by second-order or electromagnetic effects. This is a great improvement, but no convincing theoretical reason has been found for it. A possible line of approach has been indicated by Feynmann who points out that the Lagrangian for a free fermion contains the fermion mass, while that for a free boson contains the square of the boson mass. However, until further information is available, it would be better to regard the idea as an experimental hypothesis, to be confirmed or rejected when it is known how successful it is with other meson multiplets.

The first serious difficulty arises when we come to consider the mesons with $J^P = 1^-$. There is a K* of mass $892 \cdot 6 \pm 0 \cdot 5$ MeV and a ρ ($I = 1$, $Y = 0$) of mass 765 ± 10 MeV. However this time there are *two* candidates for the member with $I = Y = 0$: the ϕ of mass $1019 \cdot 5 \pm 0 \cdot 6$ MeV, and the ω with mass $783 \cdot 9 \pm 0 \cdot 3$ MeV. Let us try to use eqn (5.88) to determine which is a member of the octet. As before, we interpret M as giving the square of the mass. Now

$$\tfrac{1}{3}(4M_{K*} - M_\rho) = 0 \cdot 87 \pm 0 \cdot 07 \; (\text{GeV})^2. \tag{5.91}$$

This suggests a mass of about 930 ± 40 MeV for the $I = Y = 0$ state, and so neither the ϕ nor the ω seem to fit. The situation is not improved by interpreting M as giving the mass directly. To try to find a reason for this disappointing result, let us return to the original discussion of the octet in Section 5.2. We divided the general tensor with elements $A_j{}^p$ into an SU_3 singlet

$$S = (\sqrt{\tfrac{1}{3}})(A_1^1 + A_2^2 + A_3^3), \tag{5.92}$$

and a traceless octet. Most of the members of this octet were simply elements of A, but in order to preserve SU_2 it was necessary to introduce two linear combinations for the $Y = 0$ states.

$$I = 1 \qquad (\sqrt{\tfrac{1}{2}})(A_1^1 - A_2^2), \tag{5.93}$$

$$I = 0 \qquad (\sqrt{\tfrac{1}{6}})(A_1^1 + A_2^2 - 2A_3^3), \tag{5.94}$$

cf. eqns (5.20), (5.23), (5.25). Let us call these two states ρ, ϕ_8 respectively. Now the clue to understanding the mass discrepancy comes from observing that S, ϕ_8 both have $I = Y = 0$. They are saved from degeneracy *in pure SU_3* by the fact that the first is a singlet and the second a member of an octet. *But the mass splitting operator violates SU_3 and it is therefore possible that it can mix the two states* while still, of course, conserving isospin and hypercharge. The physical states, ϕ, ω, may in fact be linear combinations of S, ϕ_8. Since absolute phases cannot be determined, these linear combinations may be described with complete generality in terms of a mixing angle, θ, defined by the equations

$$\omega = S \cos\theta + \phi_8 \sin\theta, \qquad \phi = -S \sin\theta + \phi_8 \cos\theta, \tag{5.95}$$

or, equivalently,

$$S = \omega \cos\theta - \phi \sin\theta, \qquad \phi_8 = \omega \sin\theta + \phi \cos\theta. \tag{5.96}$$

The expectation value of the mass operator for ϕ_8 is

$$M_{\phi_8} = \langle \phi_8 | M | \phi_8 \rangle = M_\omega \sin^2\theta + M_\phi \cos^2\theta + 2\mathrm{Re}\langle \omega | M | \phi \rangle. \qquad (5.97)$$

But by definition ϕ, ω are the actual physical states and hence the mass operator produces no mixing between them. The last term of eqn (5.97) vanishes and

$$M_{\phi_8} = M_\omega \sin^2\theta + M_\phi \cos^2\theta; \qquad (5.98)$$

$$\therefore \quad 4M_{K*} = M_\rho + 3M_\omega \sin^2\theta + 3M_\phi \cos^2\theta. \qquad (5.99)$$

As it stands, eqn (5.99) can easily be satisfied by choosing a suitable value for θ. It may be regarded as a useful equation for determining θ empirically, but, unless we have other reasons for assigning a value to θ, it adds very little, beyond an extra parameter, to our theory. Fortunately it turns out that there is a very natural choice for θ. We observe that A_3^3 is, as it stands, a pure $I = Y = 0$ state. For exact SU_2 but minimum SU_3 mixing we could set

$$\phi = A_3^3. \qquad (5.100)$$

The remaining $I = Y = 0$ state would be

$$\omega = (\sqrt{\tfrac{1}{2}})(A_1^1 + A_2^2). \qquad (5.101)$$

The nine SU_2 eigenstates of the unreduced tensor, A, form what is called an *ideal nonet* with elements

$$A_1^3, A_2^3; \qquad A_1^2, (\sqrt{\tfrac{1}{2}})(A_1^1 - A_2^2), A_2^1; \qquad (\sqrt{\tfrac{1}{2}})(A_1^1 + A_2^2);$$
$$A_3^3; A_3^2, A_3^1.$$

These can be grouped into isospin multiplets with

$$(I, Y) = (\tfrac{1}{2}, 1), (1, 0), (0, 0), (0, 0), (\tfrac{1}{2}, -1). \qquad (5.102)$$

Compare this with the ideal octet given by eqn (5.26). The only mixing which has been imposed is that required to make all states pure isospin eigenstates. No purely SU_3 mixing has been included. Eqns (5.95), (5.100), (5.101) are easily solved to yield

$$\sin\theta = \sqrt{\tfrac{1}{3}} \qquad \cos\theta = \sqrt{\tfrac{2}{3}}. \qquad (5.103)$$

Using eqn (5.99)

$$4M_{K*} = M_\rho + M_\omega + 2M_\phi. \qquad (5.104)$$

In this case

$$\text{LHS} = 3 \cdot 19 \pm 0 \cdot 18 \ (\text{GeV})^2, \quad \text{RHS} = 3 \cdot 28 \pm 0 \cdot 10 \ (\text{GeV})^2. \qquad (5.105)$$

This is quite reasonable agreement and so it appears that the observed

$J^P = 1^-$ states form, to a good approximation, an ideal nonet. The reason why the 0^- mesons form an octet, while the 1^- mesons form a nonet, will emerge rather more clearly from the discussion of SU_6.

Next consider electromagnetic mass splitting. We have seen that the strong interactions do not satisfy SU_3 symmetry exactly. We must now take into account the fact that electromagnetic interactions do not satisfy it either. The clue to understanding this latter effect was given in Section 5.5. We postulated that U–spin is an exact symmetry of the electromagnetic interaction, just as isospin is an exact symmetry of the strong interaction. All members of a U–spin multiplet have the same electromagnetic properties. Further, since the charge operator commutes with all the generators of U–spin, it plays the same part in the theory of electromagnetic interactions as hypercharge plays in the theory of strong interactions. We then went on to show that the algebra of U–spin could easily be derived from the algebra of isospin by permuting the indices.

Let us apply this reasoning to electromagnetic mass splitting. The electromagnetic mass splitting operator must be a linear combination of irreducible SU_3 tensor elements. This linear combination must commute with the charge operator and with the generators of U–spin. It can therefore be expressed as the sum of the $U = Q = 0$ elements of irreducible SU_3 tensor operators with $L = U = 0, 1, 2, \ldots$. If we assume that only the first two terms of this series (from the singlet and the octet) contribute, then the formalism is exactly analogous to that for the strong interaction mass splitting. We consider the three important multiplets in turn.

1. *The singlet, S.* This can of course have no electromagnetic mass splitting.

2. *The octet*, with elements A_j^p. By analogy with eqn (5.82), we can write immediately

$$2M_{(\frac{1}{2},1)}{}^e + 2M_{(\frac{1}{2},-1)}{}^e = 3M_{(0,0)}{}^e + M_{(1,0)}{}^e, \qquad (5.106)$$

where $M_{(U,Q)}{}^e$ is the electromagnetic contribution to the mass for the elements of the U–spin multiplet with charge, Q, and U–spin, U. Unfortunately, by eqn (5.71), the state with $U = Q = 0$ does not exist physically. It is, in fact, a mixture of two physical states and so eqn (5.106) does not yield useful results. However there is a relationship that can be derived for the six pure U–spin and isospin states, which takes into account both the strong and the electromagnetic interactions. Consider the baryon octet. Remember that isospin is an exact symmetry for the strong interaction and therefore for the $J^P = \frac{1}{2}^+$ baryon octet

$$M^s(\text{n}) = M^s(\text{p}), \quad M^s(\Sigma^-) = M^s(\Sigma^+), \quad M^s(\Xi^-) = M^s(\Xi^0), \quad (5.107)$$

where M^s now represents the contributions to the mass of the particle from both the strong and semi-strong interactions. Similarly

$$M^e(\Sigma^+) = M^e(\text{p}), \quad M^e(\text{n}) = M^e(\Xi^0), \quad M^e(\Xi^-) = M^e(\Sigma^-).(5.108)$$

But of course the total mass is made up of the strong and electro-magnetic components. (We ignore the weak interaction correction.)

$$M = M^s + M^e. \tag{5.109}$$

Hence eqns (5.107), (5.108) yield

$$M(\text{p}) - M(\text{n}) = M(\Sigma^+) - M(\Sigma^-) + M(\Xi^-) - M(\Xi^0). \tag{5.110}$$

This is the famous mass relation of Coleman and Glashow (1961). It is derived without using perturbation theory and should hold to all orders in the strong and electromagnetic interactions, and also for first-order electromagnetic corrections to the strong interaction. We should therefore expect it to be more accurate than the relation, eqn (5.82), of Gell-Mann and Okubo. Substituting observed values in eqn (5.110) gives

$$\text{LHS} = -1 \cdot 29 \pm 0 \cdot 01 \text{ MeV}, \quad \text{RHS} = 1 \cdot 3 \pm 0 \cdot 7 \text{ MeV}. \tag{5.111}$$

The relation is clearly very well satisfied. The analogous equation for the $J^P = 0^-$ meson octet would be

$$M(\text{K}^+) - M(\text{K}^0) = M(\pi^+) - M(\pi^-) + M(\text{K}^-) - M(\overline{\text{K}}^0). \tag{5.112}$$

This is true but not very interesting. Since K^+, K^-; $\text{K}^0, \overline{\text{K}}^0$; π^+, π^- are all charge conjugate pairs, eqn (5.112) follows immediately from the PCT theorem and so its correctness tells us nothing about SU_3.

3. *The decuplet*, with elements A_{jkl}. Here again the result follows immediately by analogy with the discussion of strong interaction mass splitting. The electromagnetic mass splitting varies linearly with the charge, Q. It follows that the total masses for members of the decuplet are given by

$$M = M_0 + M_1 Y + M_2 Q, \tag{5.113}$$

where M_0 is the contribution to the mass from the strong interaction proper, M_1 is the contribution from the semi-strong interaction, and M_2 is the contribution from the electromagnetic interaction. Since most of the members of the decuplet are short lived, their masses are not sufficiently well-known for us to determine how well this relation holds in practice.

We remarked at the beginning of the chapter that a great many of the more interesting and important results derived from SU_3 are possible precisely because the symmetry is not exact. This section should illustrate the point. In pure SU_3, all members of a multiplet would have the same mass and so a comparison of masses would yield no useful physical information. However, since SU_3 is approximately *but only approximately* true, it provides a basic framework for classifying particles, while the systematics of symmetry breaking give useful insight into both the strong and the electromagnetic interactions. In the present section we have derived some mass formulae using plausible, but not rigorous, assumptions. The Gell–Mann–Okubo mass formula, eqn (5.82), and the rule for mass splitting within the decuplet, were derived by taking the simplest form for strong inter-action mass splitting consistent with conservation of isospin and hypercharge, and evaluating its expectation value in first-order perturbation theory. One would expect them to be at best accurate to first order and up to the level of electromagnetic mass splitting. Comparison with mass tables shows that within these limits they are correct. When applying the same reasoning to meson masses, we had to make the *ad hoc* hypothesis that the mass operator gives the square of the physical masses. But in return, we derived useful insight into the SU_3 mixing in the $J^P = 1^-$ nonet. Similar reasoning applied to electro-magnetic mass splitting was somewhat less useful, both because not all physical states are electromagnetic eigenstates, and because the splitting is only of about the same order as the uncertainty in the particle masses. However, elementary reasoning, assuming only that isospin is an exact symmetry for the strong interaction, and U–spin for the electromagnetic interaction, yielded the Coleman–Glashow relation, eqn (5.110). One would expect this to be much more accurate than any of the earlier formulae and in practice this turns out to be the case. While there is obviously a great deal more to be learned about mass systematics, these formulae are very useful and should provide a suitable point from which to proceed to further and better under-standing.

5.7. Magnetic dipole moments and selection rules

The ideas which were used in the last section to give the formulae for electromagnetic mass splitting, can also be used to give magnetic dipole moments and electromagnetic selection rules. One uses SU_3 to provide the basic framework for classifying particles, but then takes into account the fact that it is violated by the electromagnetic interaction. One assumes that U–spin is an exact symmetry of the electromagnetic interaction, just as isospin is an exact symmetry of the strong interaction, and calculates the consequences of this assumption in first-order perturbation theory. The present section gives an introduction to the method. First it calculates some relations between the magnetic dipole moments of the members of the $J^P = \frac{1}{2}^+$ baryon octet. Then it gives two examples of the consequences of U–spin symmetry for electromagnetic interactions. The reader will find other similar examples in the standard texts on particle physics.

Assuming that U–spin is an exact symmetry for the electromagnetic interaction, it follows that all members of a U–spin multiplet have the same magnetic dipole moment. In first order perturbation theory, the magnetic dipole moment operator can be expressed as the sum of the $U = Q = 0$ elements of irreducible SU_3 tensor operators with $L = U = 0, 1, 2, \ldots$. If we assume that only the first two terms of this series (from the singlet and the octet) contribute, then by analogy with eqn (5.106)

$$2\mu_{(\frac{1}{2},1)} + 2\mu_{(\frac{1}{2},-1)} = 3\mu_{(0,0)} + \mu_{(1,0)}, \tag{5.114}$$

where $\mu_{(U,Q)}$ is the magnetic dipole moment for the elements of a U–spin multiplet with charge, Q, and U–spin, U. We can derive a further useful relationship by assuming that μ is an operator which acts symmetrically on the octet, and hence that the sum of its values for all members of the octet is zero:

$$2\mu_{(\frac{1}{2},1)} + 2\mu_{(\frac{1}{2},-1)} + \mu_{(0,0)} + 3\mu_{(1,0)} = 0. \tag{5.115}$$

From eqns (5.114), (5.115), we have

$$\mu_{(0,0)} = -\mu_{(1,0)}, \qquad \mu_{(\frac{1}{2},-1)} = -\mu_{(1,0)} - \mu_{(\frac{1}{2},1)}. \tag{5.116}$$

There remains, however, the difficulty that the physical $I = Y = 0$ states are not pure U–spin eigenstates. In fact, by eqn (5.71),

$$\Sigma_U^0 = \frac{\sqrt{3}}{2}\Lambda^0 - \frac{1}{2}\Sigma^0, \qquad \Lambda_U^0 = -\frac{1}{2}\Lambda^0 - \frac{\sqrt{3}}{2}\Sigma^0, \tag{5.117}$$

$$\therefore \quad \mu_{(0,0)} = \langle \Lambda_U^0 | \mu | \Lambda_U^0 \rangle = \frac{1}{4}\mu(\Lambda^0) + \frac{3}{4}\mu(\Sigma^0) + \frac{\sqrt{3}}{2}\mu(\Lambda^0\Sigma^0), \tag{5.118}$$

where the last term is proportional to the magnetic dipole transition matrix element between Σ^0, Λ^0. Similarly

$$\mu_{(1,0)} = \tfrac{3}{4}\mu(\Lambda^0) + \tfrac{1}{4}\mu(\Sigma^0) - \frac{\sqrt{3}}{2}\mu(\Lambda^0\Sigma^0). \tag{5.119}$$

Finally, since Λ_U^0, Σ_U^0 are by definition pure U–spin eigenstates, the magnetic dipole moment operator, μ, produces no transition between them.

$$\langle \Lambda_U^0 | \mu | \Sigma_U^0 \rangle = 0,$$

$$\therefore \quad -\frac{\sqrt{3}}{4}\mu(\Lambda^0) + \frac{\sqrt{3}}{4}\mu(\Sigma^0) - \tfrac{1}{2}\mu(\Lambda^0\Sigma^0) = 0. \tag{5.120}$$

It follows from eqns (5.116–120) that we may write all the magnetic dipole moments in terms of two parameters. It is usual to choose these as the neutron and proton moments:

$$\mu(\Sigma^+) = \mu(p),$$

$$\mu(\Xi^0) = 2\mu(\Lambda^0) = -2\mu(\Sigma^0) = -\left(\frac{2}{\sqrt{3}}\right)\mu(\Lambda^0\Sigma^0) = \mu(n), \tag{5.121}$$

$$\mu(\Sigma^-) = \mu(\Xi^-) = -\mu(p) - \mu(n).$$

Indeed, it turns out that if we assume SU_6 we can go still further and express $\mu(n)$ in terms of $\mu(p)$, thus obtaining all the octet magnetic dipole moments in terms of a single parameter.

Now consider the selection rules for electromagnetic transitions. Again assuming that U–spin is an exact symmetry for these transitions, it follows that the electromagnetic transition operator has $U = 0$. It is a U–spin scalar. Electromagnetic transitions therefore satisfy the selection rule $\triangle U = \triangle U_z = 0$. This has several consequences. Consider, for instance, the following radiative transitions between the $J^P = \tfrac{3}{2}^+$ baryon decuplet and the $J^P = \tfrac{1}{2}^+$ baryon octet

$$\Xi^{*-} \to \Xi^- + \gamma \qquad Y^{*-} \to \Sigma^- + \gamma$$
$$Y^{*+} \to \Sigma^+ + \gamma \qquad N^{*+} \to p + \gamma.$$

All of these transitions conserve charge, baryon number, strangeness, etc., but the first two are transitions from a $U = \tfrac{3}{2}$ to a $U = \tfrac{1}{2}$ state and are therefore forbidden. The last two are transitions from a $U = \tfrac{1}{2}$ to a $U = \tfrac{1}{2}$ state and are therefore allowed. These predictions are well verified by experiment.

Next compare the reactions

$$\pi^0 \to 2\gamma, \qquad \eta \to 2\gamma.$$

The decay product in both cases has $U = 0$, but neither the π^0 nor the η is a pure U–spin state. However, using eqns (5.67–69) we can define a pure $U = 1$ state, $\pi_U{}^0$ say:

$$\pi_U{}^0 \equiv \frac{\sqrt{3}}{2}\eta - \tfrac{1}{2}\pi^0. \tag{5.122}$$

The decay of this state into two gammas is forbidden by U–spin conservation.

$$\langle 2\gamma | S | \pi_U{}^0 \rangle = \frac{\sqrt{3}}{2}\langle 2\gamma | S | \eta \rangle - \tfrac{1}{2}\langle 2\gamma | S | \pi^0 \rangle = 0,$$

$$\therefore \quad |\langle 2\gamma | S | \pi^0 \rangle|^2 = 3 |\langle 2\gamma | S | \eta \rangle|^2. \tag{5.123}$$

Thus the selection rule gives a relation between the rates of the two decays.

This chapter has aimed to do little more than discuss the postulates which are made in SU_3 theory, and to list some of the methods which can be used to work out the consequences of these postulates. The choice of examples has necessarily been eclectic. However, the reader will find that the ideas of SU_3 permeate the whole of particle physics and the introduction given in this chapter should allow him to follow the more detailed discussions which he will find throughout the literature.

Problems

Consider the irreducible rank-4 tensor with elements A_{jk}^{pq}.

(a) What is its dimension?

(b) Use the methods outlined in Sections 5.2, 5.5 to give the values of I, I_z, U, U_z, V, V_z, Y, Q for the element A_{11}^{33}.

(c) Draw the weight diagram for A. Show how this weight diagram could be used to help solve problem (b).

(d) A can be obtained by reducing the general tensor A' with elements, A'_{jk}^{pq}, where j, k, p, q can all run from one to three. Indicate how this is done. Amongst the irreducible tensors obtained from this reduction are two SU_3 singlets. Express them explicitly as a linear combination of the elements of A'.

(e) Give the dimensions of the irreducible multiplets which can be obtained by reducing the direct product of A and the irreducible octet, B. Show that the same decomposition is obtained whether the weight diagram for A is superimposed on the Speiser point corresponding to B, or the weight diagram for B is superimposed on the Speiser point corresponding to A.

(f) Express the $I = Y = 0$ element of A as a linear combination of the elements of A'.

(g) Suppose that the strong interaction mass splitting operator contains the $I = Y = 0$ elements of the irreducible tensor operators with $L = U = 0$, 1, 2 (not just 0, 1). Derive a mass formula for the baryon decuplet.

6

THE SYMMETRY SU_6

The success of SU_2 and SU_3 led naturally to an active search for yet higher symmetries. This chapter gives an introduction to one of these. It starts by emphasizing that much of the value of higher symmetries lies in the insight which they give into baryon systematics, and that this insight is possible precisely because the symmetries are not exact. It then shows how intrinsic spin and SU_3 can be incorporated into a higher symmetry called SU_6. Next it discusses the SU_6 generators and indicates which multiplets are permitted and what are the quantum numbers of their elements. It argues that, while SU_6 can be useful, it is not as important or as well founded as SU_3. For this reason, the treatment is much less detailed and the reader is referred to the literature for further and more advanced discussions.

6.1. Intrinsic spin and SU_3

We pointed out at the beginning of the last chapter that the motive and the approach of the search for higher symmetries are rather different from the motive and the approach of isospin theory. Isospin theory started with a symmetry transformation which had a fairly obvious physical interpretation and it postulated that the strong interaction is invariant under this transformation. This led naturally to a discussion of the relevant observables and conservation laws. On the other hand, the main motive for introducing higher symmetries is that they allow us to describe the systematics of groups of particles which have certain clearly defined properties in common, and certain other properties which differ in a way which can be calculated. One therefore begins by introducing a rather abstract symmetry transformation and postulating that to a first approximation the strong interaction is invariant under this transformation. The physical interpretation remains unclear until observables have been associated with particular generators or com-binations of generators. When this has been done, particles can be classified into multiplets, and the properties of the members of each multiplet can be divided immediately into two classes. Properties in the first class can be calculated using the algebra of the symmetry; properties of the second class are common to all members of the multiplet. We saw in the last chapter that SU_3 gives a very good account of the quantized properties of the second class, but that other properties, such as mass and magnetic dipole moment which can vary continuously, must be calculated by approximate methods. Some of these methods were described and interesting relations were derived.

Now it is instructive to consider what would happen if SU_3 were exact. Clearly all members of any given SU_3 multiplet would have the same mass and all members of the $J^P = \frac{1}{2}^+$ baryon octet would be stable. If the members of the $J^P = \frac{3}{2}^+$ baryon decuplet were sufficiently massive, then each could decay into a member of the $J^P = \frac{1}{2}^+$ octet plus a meson. And this decay could proceed by the strong interaction for *all* members of the decuplet. If the N^{*-} could decay into a neutron and π^-, then the Ω^- could decay into a Ξ^0 and K^-. How then would one distinguish between the various members of an SU_3 multiplet? It would obviously be possible to identify different charge states by observing tracks in a bubble chamber. But how could one distinguish between different hypercharge states? The usual differences between the decay rates of strange and non-strange particles would have vanished. In fact, a little reflection will convince the reader that hypercharge would not be observable at all. The $J^P = \frac{1}{2}^+$ octet would apparently consist simply of three particles with charges $\pm e$, 0 and the decuplet of four particles with charges $2e$, $\pm e$, 0. SU_3 would never have been discovered.

The reader may care to amuse himself by thinking through the consequences which would follow if other symmetries were exact. Consider for instance the spatial symmetry which leads to the concept of intrinsic spin. If this symmetry were broken neither by coupling to external electromagnetic fields nor by coupling to orbital angular momentum, then the Zeeman and Stark effects, fine, and hyperfine structure would all vanish and there would be no way in which intrinsic spin could be detected. The result is in fact completely general. The theory of any symmetry depends in an essential way on the existence of properties which can be distinguished physically. It then postulates that these distinctions are unimportant in certain interactions. But a classification symmetry which was really exact for all possible inter-actions would have no physical consequences at all and would never be discovered. It follows that the search for symmetries must be carried out in a fairly narrow range. Any useful symmetry must be broken in order to give it physical content, but it must still be sufficiently accurate to be a good approximation to nature. Intrinsic spin and isospin are almost ideal. Both are broken at about the one per cent level, the former by spin-orbit coupling and the latter by the electromagnetic interaction. SU_3 is less satisfactory. The symmetry breaking is large, and in particular the mass splitting of the meson multiplets is comparable with the meson masses themselves. In SU_6 the symmetry breaking is even more drastic. It is mainly worth discussing for the insight which it gives when one is trying to *explain* certain observed results. Its value as an explicit *predictive* theory is very small.

With these preliminary remarks, we are ready to discuss the basic idea of SU_6 and some of its simpler consequences. We have seen that SU_3 is very successful in relating the internal quantum numbers of particles—charge, hypercharge, isospin and so on—but that it tells us nothing about the spatial properties—spin and angular momentum. We have, however, also seen that total angular momentum is conserved in strong interactions and that it can be treated by SU_2. Further than this, *if we neglect spin-orbit coupling*, then both intrinsic spin and orbital angular momentum, taken individually, are conserved and can be treated by SU_2. The former depends on the intrinsic spatial properties of particles, the latter on their dynamic states. Thus in this limit the strong interaction satisfies three separate symmetries: SU_3 for internal quantum numbers and SU_2 for intrinsic spin and orbital angular momentum. The first two are intrinsic, the last dynamic. The obvious next step is to try to combine the two intrinsic symmetries into the larger SU_6.

Now SU_6 implies much more than simply SU_2 and SU_3 taken together, just as SU_3 implies much more than isospin and hypercharge taken together. One is assuming that changes in internal quantum numbers and changes in spin state can be treated on a symmetrical footing. The number of generators is $6^2 - 1 = 35$ as against the $3 + 8 = 11$ for SU_2 and SU_3 (cf. the discussion in Section 5.1). Twenty-four generators are entirely new. But there are undoubtedly problems. In the first place, such a mixture of spatial and non-spatial properties is inherently implausible. Spin is a quantity very different in kind from the internal quantum numbers. It seems unlikely that one can treat them all in an entirely symmetric fashion and, indeed, some of the generators correspond to very odd physical operations. In the second place, the invariance under changes of spin state alone is a poor approximation to the physical fact. The strong interaction is known to produce powerful spin-orbit coupling and it is difficult to find examples of interactions which can be discussed in terms of conservation of spin alone. It is of course perfectly possible to construct potentials which satisfy this condition—any purely central potential would do—but they seem to be a poor approximation to the potentials which occur in nature. Finally, the concept of a non-coupled intrinsic spin is non-relativistic and one would therefore expect SU_6 to be valid, if at all, only as a non-relativistic theory.

However despite these objections, SU_6 has achieved striking successes and is worth discussing provided that it is not pushed too far. We start as usual by assuming that strong interactions are invariant under transformations of the form (4.80), where now the T_j^p are special unitary matrices with six rows and six columns. Next, we require thirty-five linearly independent hermitian traceless matrices to act as generators. They can be obtained conveniently by combining the spin generators, (4.48), with the SU_3 generators, (5.2). For instance

$$\sigma_x \times \lambda_j = \tfrac{1}{2}\hbar \begin{pmatrix} 0 & \lambda_j \\ \lambda_j & 0 \end{pmatrix}, \qquad \sigma_y \times \lambda_j = \tfrac{1}{2}\mathrm{i}\hbar \begin{pmatrix} 0 & -\lambda_j \\ \lambda_j & 0 \end{pmatrix}, \qquad (6.1)$$

where the λ_j are, of course, 3×3 matrices and the symbol 0 is used to represent a 3×3 matrix with all elements zero. A complete set of thirty-five generators would have the form

$$I \times \lambda_j, \qquad \sigma_p \times I, \qquad \sigma_p \times \lambda_j, \qquad (6.2)$$

where I as usual represents the unit matrix. The interpretation of these matrices now follows from a knowledge of SU_2 and SU_3. The first group contains the pure SU_3 generators, the second group the pure spin generators, and the third group combinations of SU_3 and spin generators.

6.2. Multiplets and their quantum numbers

Once again, multiplets can be represented by irreducible tensors. These tensors have the usual form, (4.78), but now each index can take any value between one and six. The general tensor can be reduced using the δ tensor and hence all irreducible tensors are traceless (cf. Section 4.4). The symmetry properties of the indices, however, are less simple. We have two ϵ tensors

$$\epsilon_{jklmnp}, \qquad \epsilon^{jklmnp}. \qquad (6.3)$$

The first transforms n totally antisymmetric upper indices into $6 - n$ totally antisymmetric lower indices. The second does the reverse. Clearly a reduction occurs only if $n \geqslant 4$. For instance, ϵ would transform two antisymmetric upper indices to four antisymmetric lower indices. Not only has no reduction occurred, but the new tensor is still not symmetric. Thus irreducible SU_6 tensors of low rank are not necessarily symmetric in their upper and lower indices. Nevertheless they still have definite symmetry properties. To see this, notice that all permutation symmetries are preserved under the transformation (4.80). For instance if a tensor, A, is antisymmetric under exchange of the first two upper indices, then the transformed tensor, A', is antisymmetric also. This means that even if not all tensors can be reduced to totally symmetric linear combinations, they can still be separated into sets of elements such that all the elements in each set have the *same* symmetry. When this has been done each element will transform under SU_6 into a linear combination of the other elements. Each set is in fact a new reduced tensor. We have thus introduced another method for reducing tensors. It was irrelevant for SU_2 and SU_3 since our methods there guaranteed that all tensors would be symmetric. But it is highly important in SU_6.

We are now in a position to calculate the dimensions (i.e. the number of elements) of some SU_6 tensors. We cannot, however, reduce the result to a single equation analogous to eqn (5.10) since we must treat the various possible symmetries separately. First, consider the *totally symmetric tensors*. An element of a multiplet can be distinguished by the number of ones, twos, and so on amongst its upper and lower indices, but not by the order in which they occur. The number of different choices for the L lower indices is

$$N_L = \binom{L+5}{5},$$ (6.4)

where

$$\binom{a}{b} \equiv \frac{a!}{(a-b)!\,b!}.$$ (6.5)

Similarly

$$N_U = \binom{U+5}{5}.$$ (6.6)

The dimension of the multiplet is equal to $N_L N_U$ less the number of constraint equations imposed by the requirement that all traces be zero (cf. the discussion in Section 5.1). Each trace equation has the form

$$\delta_j^q A_{pq...t}^{jk...m} = 0,$$ (6.7)

and there must clearly be $N_{(L-1)} N_{(U-1)}$ of these. Hence the dimension of the multiplet is given by

$$D = N_L N_U - N_{(L-1)} N_{(U-1)} = \binom{L+4}{4} \binom{U+4}{4} \left(1 + \frac{L+U}{5}\right) \quad (6.8)$$

(cf. eqn (5.10)). The dimensions of some multiplets of this type are

S	1	A_j	6
A_{jk}	21	A^p_j	35
A_{jkl}	56		

Next consider the *totally antisymmetric tensors*. In this case, no number may appear more than once amongst either the upper or the lower indices, and thus an element of a multiplet can be distinguished by *whether* the numbers one, two, and so on appear amongst its upper or lower indices. The number of different choices for the L lower indices is

$$N'_L = \binom{6}{L}, \quad (6.9)$$

and, by the reasoning used above, the dimension of the multiplet is

$$D' = N'_L N'_U - N'_{(L-1)} N'_{(U-1)} = \binom{7}{L} \binom{7}{U} \left(1 - \frac{L+U}{7}\right). \quad (6.10)$$

The dimensions of some multiplets of this type are

S	1	A_j	6
A'_{jk}	15	A^p_j	35
A'_{jkl}	20	A'^p_{jklm}	70

Notice that the total number of indices with this type of tensor cannot exceed six. For obvious reasons, S, A_j, A^p_j appear in both lists. Using similar methods, one could set up multiplets with more complicated symmetry properties. However this is not necessary for our present purposes.

Next consider the quantum numbers of these multiplets. We could determine complete sets of quantum numbers for the SU_6 multiplets by constructing the operators corresponding to observables and applying them to each element in turn. This procedure worked very well for SU_3. However in this case it is simpler to remark that, since SU_6 contains both SU_2 and SU_3, each SU_6 multiplet can be decomposed into simple $SU_2 \times SU_3$ multiplets. Once the decomposition is known, a complete account of the quantum numbers follows immediately.

Let us write these $SU_2 \times SU_3$ multiplets as (N, M), where N is the dimension of the SU_2 multiplet and M is the dimension of the SU_3 multiplet. (The whole procedure is analogous to our decomposition of SU_3 multiplets into $SU_2 \times SU_1$ multiplets labelled by the quantum numbers I and Y.) Consider some examples.

1. *The singlet*, S, is a spinless boson with all SU_3 quantum numbers zero.

2. *The sextet*, with elements, A_j, consists of a single $SU_2 \times SU_3$ multiplet and has quantum numbers $(2, 3)$. The elements thus correspond to spin $\frac{1}{2}$ quarks. Similarly, the elements, A^j, of the anti-sextet correspond to spin $\frac{1}{2}$ anti-quarks. These are the simplest non-trivial SU_6 multiplets and for this reason it is usually assumed that any physical quarks would be spin $\frac{1}{2}$ fermions. They would be very odd fermions however, since, as we saw in Section 5.3, the complex symmetries permitted by SU_6 imply that physical multi-quark states are not necessarily totally antisymmetric under exchange.

3. *The thirty-five-plet*, with elements, A_j^p, has zero trace. It may be obtained from the general mixed rank-two tensor with elements, B_j^p, by separating off the singlet

$$S = \delta_p^j B_j^p \tag{6.11}$$

(cf. the discussion of the octet in Section 5.2). It is an irreducible SU_6 multiplet and could, if necessary, be expressed as the sum of $SU_2 \times SU_3$ multiplets using the standard reduction procedure. This procedure should now be familiar after the discussion of SU_2 and SU_3, but it is undoubtedly somewhat tedious (Van Hove 1965). It is much simpler to write B^p in the form $(2, 3) \times (2, \bar{3})$ and to use the familiar rules for taking direct products of SU_2 and SU_3 multiplets:

$$(2, 3) \times (2, \bar{3}) = (2 \times 2, 3 \times \bar{3}) = (3 + 1, 8 + 1)$$

$$= (3, 8) + (1, 8) + (3, 1) + (1, 1). \tag{6.12}$$

The last term is obviously the singlet and so the thirty-five-plet contains three SU_3 multiplets: a spin 1 octet, a spin 0 octet and a spin 1 singlet:

$$35 = (3, 8) + (1, 8) + (3, 1) \tag{6.13}$$

(cf. eqn (5.26)). On the quark model, one would interpret this as a quark–anti-quark system and its elements as mesons. It is very striking that the thirty-five-plet exactly contains the meson states which were discussed in Section 5.6. It also provides a rather natural explanation

12

of the fact that the $J^P = 1^-$ mesons form an approximately ideal nonet while the $J^P = 0^-$ mesons form an octet. The $J^P = 1^-$ octet and singlet lie in the same SU_6 multiplet, while the $J^P = 0^-$ octet is in a different SU_6 multiplet from any $J^P = 0^-$ singlets.

4. *The general covariant rank-two tensor* with elements A_{jk}, can be reduced immediately by writing it as the sum of a symmetric and an antisymmetric tensor:

$$A_{jk} = \tfrac{1}{2}(A_{jk} + A_{kj}) + \tfrac{1}{2}(A_{jk} - A_{kj}) \equiv B_{jk} + C_{jk}, \qquad (6.14)$$

where eqn (6.14) defines the tensors B, C. The symmetric tensor, B, is the twenty-one-plet and the antisymmetric tensor, C, is the fifteen-plet. (Note that the total dimension is, of course, thirty-six.) The $SU_2 \times SU_3$ decomposition of B, C is easily obtained by writing A in the form

$$(2, 3) \times (2, 3) = (2 \times 2, 3 \times 3) = (3 + 1, 6 + \bar{3})$$

$$= (3, 6) + (1, 6) + (3, \bar{3}) + (1, \bar{3}). \qquad (6.15)$$

By counting multiplicities it is obvious that the only possible assignment is

$$21 = (3, 6) + (1, \bar{3}), \qquad 15 = (1, 6) + (3, \bar{3}). \qquad (6.16)$$

Thus the twenty-one-plet contains a spin 1 sextet and a spin 0 anti-triplet, while the fifteen-plet contains a spin 0 sextet and a spin 1 anti-triplet. None of the corresponding states has integral charge and none has been observed so far. On the quark model they would be the two-quark states.

5. *The general covariant rank-three tensor*, with elements A_{jkl}. The first step in the reduction follows the method used to derive eqn (6.14). We define two new tensors D, E. D is symmetric in the first two indices and E is antisymmetric.

$$A_{jkl} = \tfrac{1}{2}(A_{jkl} + A_{kjl}) + \tfrac{1}{2}(A_{jkl} - A_{kjl}) \equiv D_{jkl} + E_{jkl}. \qquad (6.17)$$

Next, D can be reduced by separating out the component which is antisymmetric in k, l.

$$F_j^{mnpq} \equiv \epsilon^{klmnpq} D_{jkl}; \qquad (6.18)$$

F has four totally antisymmetric upper indices and one lower index. It follows that it must be a seventy-plet. The remaining tensor has three totally symmetric lower indices and so is a fifty-six-plet. D has 21×6 components and we may summarize this step in the form

$$21 \times 6 = 70 + 56. \qquad (6.19)$$

Once again, the quantum numbers follow by considering the $SU_2 \times SU_3$ decomposition. Using eqn (6.16)

$$\{(3,\, 6) + (1,\, \bar{3})\} \times (2,\, 3) = (3 \times 2,\, 6 \times 3) + (1 \times 2,\, 3 \times \bar{3})$$
$$= (4 + 2,\, 10 + 8) + (2,\, 8 + 1)$$
$$= (4,\, 10) + (4,\, 8) + (2,\, 10) + (2,\, 8)$$
$$+ (2,\, 8) + (2,\, 1). \tag{6.20}$$

By counting multiplicities, there is again only one possible assignment:

$$70 = (4,\, 8) + (2,\, 10) + (2,\, 8) + (2,\, 1),$$
$$56 = (4,\, 10) + (2,\, 8). \tag{6.21}$$

E can be reduced in a similar fashion. Since it is totally antisymmetric in the first two indices, it can be re-written

$$E'^{mnpq}_{l} = \epsilon^{jkmnpq} E_{jkl}. \tag{6.22}$$

Next, we can separate out the trace:

$$G^{npq} \equiv \delta^l_m E'^{mnpq}_{l}. \tag{6.23}$$

Eqn (6.23) defines a new covariant rank-three tensor, G. It is clearly the twenty-plet. The remaining elements of E' form an irreducible tensor with four totally antisymmetric upper indices, one lower index, and zero trace. This is another seventy-plet. E and E' each have 15×6 components and we can summarize this step in the form

$$15 \times 6 = 70 + 20, \tag{6.24}$$

and obtain the quantum numbers by considering the $SU_2 \times SU_3$ decomposition

$$\{(1,\, 6) + (3,\, \bar{3})\} \times (2,\, 3) = (1 \times 2,\, 6 \times 3) + (3 \times 2,\, \bar{3} \times 3)$$
$$= (2,\, 10) + (2,\, 8) + (4,\, 8) + (2,\, 8) + (4,\, 1) + (2,\, 1). \tag{6.25}$$

Comparison with eqn (6.21) shows immediately that

$$20 = (2,\, 8) + (4,\, 1). \tag{6.26}$$

Thus the reduction of A_{jkl} can be summarized as

$$216 = 56 + 70 + 70 + 20. \tag{6.27}$$

Note that the total dimensions of the left and right sides are equal. On the quark model, these multiplets would all be composed of baryons.

Of the four, the totally symmetric fifty-six-plet is of particular interest since it includes a $J^P = \frac{1}{2}^+$ octet and a $J^P = \frac{3}{2}^+$ decuplet and these are precisely the baryon states which were discussed in Section 5.6. This, like the assignment of the meson thirty-five-plet, is one of the more notable successes of SU_6.

This concludes our brief introduction to SU_6. It has necessarily been far from complete. Much work has been done on mass formulae and electromagnetic effects and there have been many striking successes. It is probably fair to say that there have also been a rather larger number of striking failures than for SU_3. The literature about the higher symmetries is vast and the reader will find a great deal of further useful information in Van Hove (1965), de Swart (1963, 1964, 1966), Feld (1967), Brene and Hellesen (1965), Gell–Mann and Ne'eman (1964). He should also be in a position to tackle later papers in which these ideas are applied to more specific problems.

Our treatment of SU_3 covered tensors with sufficiently high rank to include all particles which have been discovered so far. Our treatment of SU_6 has now included all the more familiar baryons and mesons discussed in Section 5.6. In order to describe states with $J > \frac{3}{2}$, it would be necessary to reduce general tensors with rank greater than three. This is possible, but not necessarily very useful, since the dimensions of such tensors rapidly become very large indeed and their analysis correspondingly more complex. In order to include baryons with $J = \frac{5}{2}$, for instance, one would have to introduce the general mixed rank-five tensor with components A^p_{jklm}. There are 7776 components altogether, and the identification of the physical states corresponding to these components with elements of a single tensor seems almost impossibly difficult. Further, in addition to singlets, octets, and decuplets, it contains SU_3 tensors of higher rank. Some of their elements have exotic quantum numbers and there is still no evidence that exotic states exist. In short, SU_6 does not seem to provide an all-embracing scheme for classifying particles, even if only quantized properties are included. The present evidence suggests that its predictions are too general to be true without restriction, and that even if they were true they would be too complicated to be useful.

We must therefore look to other schemes. It may be that these schemes will also be based on approximate symmetries, but we have seen that the type of analysis discussed in the last two chapters works in only a narrow range. The symmetry must be broken, but not by too much. It may well be that we have reached the limit of understanding which is possible by such methods and that the next step must be towards dynamical theories which aim to relate states of higher to states of lower spin. It is too early to predict the outcome of the search, but a study of baryon and meson systematics—which particles exist and why—remains one of the most important tasks of particle physics.

Problems

(a) Write down the SU_6 operators corresponding to hypercharge and the third components of spin and isospin.

(b) Hence give quantum numbers for the elements of the totally symmetric fifty-six-plet.

(c) Show how these can be grouped into spin and isospin eigenstates.

(d) Hence show how they can be separated into two SU_3 multiplets with quantum numbers $(4,10)$ and $(2,8)$.

SOLUTIONS TO PROBLEMS

Chapter 1

(a)
$$HR = \begin{pmatrix} -4 & -4\sqrt{3} & 8(\sqrt{3}i) \\ -4\sqrt{3} & -12 & 24i \\ -8(\sqrt{3}i) & -24i & -48 \end{pmatrix} E_0\hbar = RH.$$

Hence, by eqn (1.90), R is conserved. After finding HR, some labour may be saved by noting that it is hermitian.

$$\therefore \quad RH = R^\dagger H^\dagger = (HR)^\dagger = HR.$$

(b) Using eqn (1.69)
$$|R - \lambda I| = -\lambda^3 + \lambda\hbar^2 = 0$$

Hence eigenvalues are $r_1 = -\hbar$, $r_2 = 0$, $r_3 = \hbar$.

(c) To tackle this, either solve directly for the ψ_j, E_j, or use eqn (1.69) to show that the eigenvalues of H are 0, $16E_0$, $64E_0$. In order to determine which of these corresponds to each value of R, note that the eigenvalues of HR are 0, 0, $-64E_0\hbar$.

$$\therefore \quad E_1 = 64E_0, \quad E_2 = 16E_0, \quad E_3 = 0.$$

(d)
$$\langle \phi|H|\phi \rangle = 8E_0 \qquad \langle \phi|R|\phi \rangle = \tfrac{1}{2}\hbar$$
$$\langle \chi|H|\chi \rangle = 40E_0 \qquad \langle \chi|R|\chi \rangle = -\tfrac{1}{2}\hbar$$

Hence, expanding ϕ, χ in terms of ψ_1, ψ_2, ψ_3 as in eqn (1.18), and using the normalization condition, (1.16), it follows that

$$\phi = (\sqrt{\tfrac{1}{2}})(e^{i\alpha}\psi_2 + e^{i\beta}\psi_3) \qquad \chi = (\sqrt{\tfrac{1}{2}})(e^{i\gamma}\psi_1 + e^{i\delta}\psi_2),$$

where α, β, γ, δ are real. Now taking the inner product

$$\langle \phi|\chi \rangle = \tfrac{1}{2} = \tfrac{1}{2}e^{i(\delta - \beta)}.$$

Hence $e^{i\delta} = e^{i\beta}$, but the constants, α, β, γ are undetermined.

(e) By eqn (1.9), $P = |\langle \phi|\chi \rangle|^2 = \tfrac{1}{4}$.

(f) The most general symmetry operator, T, corresponding to R is given by eqn (1.157). This is most easily expressed in matrix form in the basis for which R is diagonal.

$$T = \begin{pmatrix} e^{i\lambda} & 0 & 0 \\ 0 & 1 & 0 \\ 0 & 0 & e^{i\theta} \end{pmatrix},$$

where $\lambda \equiv f(-\hbar)$, $\theta \equiv f(\hbar)$. Thus λ, θ are arbitrary real constants. To express T in the original basis note that

$$T = (2 - \tfrac{1}{2}e^{i\lambda} - \tfrac{1}{2}e^{i\theta})I + (-1 + \tfrac{1}{2}e^{i\lambda} + \tfrac{1}{2}e^{i\theta})H/16E_0 + (-2 + \tfrac{1}{2}e^{i\lambda} + \tfrac{3}{2}e^{i\theta})R/\hbar.$$

But this equation remains true in *any* basis. Hence, in the original basis

$$T = \tfrac{1}{16}\begin{pmatrix} 3 + e^{i\lambda} + 12\,e^{i\theta} & (\sqrt{3})(3 + e^{i\lambda} - 4\,e^{i\theta}) & 2(\sqrt{3})i(1 - e^{i\lambda}) \\ (\sqrt{3})(3 + e^{i\lambda} - 4\,e^{i\theta}) & 9 + 3\,e^{i\lambda} + 4\,e^{i\theta} & 6i(1 - e^{i\lambda}) \\ 2(\sqrt{3})i(-1 + e^{i\lambda}) & 6i(-1 + e^{i\lambda}) & 4 + 12\,e^{i\lambda} \end{pmatrix}.$$

To show that T is unitary, simply multiply out.

Chapter 2

1. (i) Rate (a) = Rate (c), Rate (b) = Rate (d).
   (ii) The same.
   (iii) Rate (a) + Rate (b) = Rate (c) + Rate (d).

2. (b) $\langle \pi\pi\gamma_+ |t|K^+ \rangle = e^{i\alpha} \langle \pi\pi\gamma_- |t|K^+ \rangle$ where α is real.
   (c) CPT $\langle \pi\pi\gamma_+ |t|K^+ \rangle = \langle K^- |t|\bar{\pi}\bar{\pi}\gamma_- \rangle$ where the bar denotes the charge conjugate particle.
   (d) Write t as the sum of an hermitian and an anti-hermitian part.

$$t = t_{\rm H} + t_{\rm A}$$

   Hence show that

$$|\langle \pi\pi\gamma|t|K^+ \rangle| = |\langle \bar{\pi}\bar{\pi}\gamma|t|K^- \rangle|$$

   only if $t_{\rm A}$ is zero.

Chapter 3

1. Σ^0, K^0 parities of p, n, Λ,
   ρ^0 parity of p,
   ρ^+ parities of p, n,
   η none.

2. Parities could be assigned to $e^\pm$ and $\mu^\pm$, but not to any of the neutrinos. Two definitions would be needed, one for the electrons and one for the muons.

Chapter 4

1. Using eqn (4.47), direction cosines are

   (a) $\frac{2}{3}$, $-\frac{2}{3}$, $\frac{1}{3}$,   (b) $0, 1, 0$.

2. Follow method outlined in Section 4.2.

3.
$$J_x = \begin{pmatrix} 0 & \frac{\sqrt{3}}{2} & 0 & 0 \\ \frac{\sqrt{3}}{2} & 0 & 1 & 0 \\ 0 & 1 & 0 & \frac{\sqrt{3}}{2} \\ 0 & 0 & \frac{\sqrt{3}}{2} & 0 \end{pmatrix}\hbar, \quad J_y = \begin{pmatrix} 0 & -\frac{\sqrt{3}}{2} & 0 & 0 \\ \frac{\sqrt{3}}{2} & 0 & -1 & 0 \\ 0 & 1 & 0 & -\frac{\sqrt{3}}{2} \\ 0 & 0 & \frac{\sqrt{3}}{2} & 0 \end{pmatrix}i\hbar,$$

$$J_z = \begin{pmatrix} \frac{3}{2} & 0 & 0 & 0 \\ 0 & \frac{1}{2} & 0 & 0 \\ 0 & 0 & -\frac{1}{2} & 0 \\ 0 & 0 & 0 & -\frac{3}{2} \end{pmatrix}\hbar.$$

4. First define $B^p \equiv \epsilon^{jk}A^p_{jk}$,

   $\therefore$ $B^1 = (\sqrt{\frac{1}{2}})(A^1_{12} - A^1_{21})$, $B^2 = (\sqrt{\frac{1}{2}})(A^2_{12} - A^2_{21})$, a doublet.

   Next define $C_k \equiv \delta^j_p A^p_{jk}$,

   $C_1 = (\sqrt{\frac{1}{2}})(A^1_{11} + A^2_{21})$, $C_2 = (\sqrt{\frac{1}{2}})(A^1_{12} + A^2_{22})$, a doublet.

   Group the remaining elements according to their third components of isospin. They form a quartet.

   A^2_{11}, $(\sqrt{\frac{1}{3}})(A^1_{11} - A^2_{12} - A^2_{21})$, $(\sqrt{\frac{1}{3}})(A^2_{22} - A^1_{21} - A^1_{12})$, A^1_{22}.

5. Total isospin of each is 1 (half number of indices).
Interaction state tensor has elements $A_{jk}B_{pq}$.

Reduction

Step 1:

$$C_{kq} = \epsilon^{jp}A_{jk}B_{pq} = A_{1k}B_{2q} - A_{2k}B_{1q}.$$

Step 2:

$$S = \epsilon^{kq}C_{kq} = [A_{11}B_{22} - A_{21}B_{12} - A_{12}B_{21} + A_{22}B_{11}] \times \text{normalizing factor}$$
$$= \tfrac{1}{2}(A_{11}B_{22} - 2A_{12}B_{12} + A_{22}B_{11}).$$

S is a *scalar* and so has $I = I_z = 0$.

Step 3: The remaining elements of C form an irreducible multiplet, C' say

$$C'_{11} = C_{11} = \left(\frac{1}{\sqrt{2}}\right)(A_{11}B_{12} - A_{12}B_{11}), \qquad I_z = 1;$$

$$C'_{12} = \left(\frac{1}{\sqrt{2}}\right)(A_{11}B_{22} - A_{22}B_{11}), \qquad I_z = 0;$$

$$C'_{22} = C_{22} = \left(\frac{1}{\sqrt{2}}\right)(A_{12}B_{22} - A_{22}B_{12}), \qquad I_z = -1;$$

C' has $I = 1$.

Step 4: The remaining elements of AB form a further irreducible multiplet

$$\begin{aligned}
D_{1111} &= A_{11}B_{11}, & I_z &= 2; \\
D_{1112} &= (\sqrt{\tfrac{1}{2}})(A_{11}B_{12} + A_{12}B_{11}), & I_z &= 1; \\
D_{1122} &= (\sqrt{\tfrac{1}{3}})(A_{11}B_{22} + A_{12}B_{12} + A_{22}B_{11}), & I_z &= 0; \\
D_{1222} &= (\sqrt{\tfrac{1}{2}})(A_{12}B_{22} + A_{22}B_{12}), & I_z &= -1; \\
D_{2222} &= A_{22}B_{22}, & I_z &= -2.
\end{aligned}$$

These linear combinations are chosen by noting
1. That we can only mix in states of a given I_z
2. That all states must be orthogonal to S and to the components of C'.
D has $I = 2$.

6. Write

$$U = \begin{pmatrix} U^1_1 & U^2_1 \\ U^1_2 & U^2_2 \end{pmatrix}$$

and solve directly.

7. Since the η decays into two gamma rays, it must be even under C. Since it is an isospin scalar, it must be invariant under all isospin rotations. It follows that it has positive G-parity. Two-pion states cannot have $J^P = 0^-$ and hence this decay is forbidden for strong and electromagnetic interactions. Decay into three pions is forbidden for strong interactions (G-parity) but can occur electromagnetically.

Chapter 5

(a) 27.

(b) $I = I_z = U = U_z = Q = 1$, $V = Y = 2$, $V_z = -2$.

(c) See Fig 5.6(a).

(d) $\tfrac{1}{3}(A'^{11}_{11} + A'^{12}_{12} + A'^{13}_{13} + A'^{21}_{21} + A'^{22}_{22} + A'^{23}_{23} + A'^{31}_{31} + A'^{32}_{32} + A'^{33}_{33})$

$\tfrac{1}{3}(A'^{11}_{11} + A'^{12}_{21} + A'^{13}_{31} + A'^{21}_{12} + A'^{22}_{22} + A'^{23}_{32} + A'^{31}_{13} + A'^{32}_{23} + A'^{33}_{33})$.

(e) $64 + 35 + \overline{35} + 27 + 27 + 10 + \overline{10} + 8$.

(f) First, define a new tensor, D, with elements

$$D_{jk}^{pq} = \tfrac{1}{2}(A_{jk}^{\prime pq} + A_{jk}^{\prime qp} + A_{kj}^{\prime pq} + A_{kj}^{\prime qp}).$$

By eqn (5.72) the $I = Y = 0$ element of A must have the form $\Sigma_{jk} a_{jk} D_{jk}^{jk}$, where the a_{jk} are expansion coefficients. Using eqn (5.16) show that the following linear combinations of the D_{jk}^{jk} have $I = 0$.

$$(\sqrt{\tfrac{1}{6}})(D_{11}^{11} + D_{22}^{22} + 2D_{12}^{12}), \quad (\sqrt{\tfrac{1}{2}})(D_{13}^{13} + D_{23}^{23}), \quad D_{33}^{33}.$$

But all elements of A must have zero trace.

$$a_{11} + a_{12} + a_{13} = a_{12} + a_{22} + a_{23} = a_{13} + a_{23} + a_{33} = 0.$$

Hence the $I = Y = 0$ element of A is

$$\frac{1}{2\sqrt{15}}(D_{11}^{11} + D_{22}^{22} + 2D_{12}^{12} - 3D_{13}^{13} - 3D_{23}^{23} + 6D_{33}^{33}).$$

This is readily expanded in terms of the A'.

(g) By analogy with eqn (5.77), the mass of the element, A_{jkl}, of the decuplet is

$$M = M_0 + A^{*\alpha kl} M_{\alpha}^{\alpha'} A_{\alpha' kl} + A^{*\alpha\beta l} D_{\alpha\beta}^{\alpha'\beta'} A_{\alpha'\beta' l},$$

where $M_{\alpha}^{\alpha'}$, $D_{\alpha\beta}^{\alpha'\beta'}$ are the $I = Y = 0$ elements of the irreducible tensor operators with $L = U = 1, 2$. Hence the masses are as follows

$A_{111}, A_{112}, A_{122}, A_{222}$	$M_0 + 3c_1 + 3c_2$
$A_{113}, A_{123}, A_{223}$	$M_0 \quad\quad -5c_2$
A_{133}, A_{233}	$M_0 - 3c_1 - 3c_2$
A_{333}	$M_0 - 6c_1 + 9c_2$

Hence, eliminating M_0, c_1, c_2.

$$M_N{}^* - 3M_Y{}^* + 3M\Xi^* - M\Omega = 0.$$

Chapter 6

(b)

I_z	Y	$J_z = \tfrac{3}{2}$	$J_z = \tfrac{1}{2}$	$J_z = -\tfrac{1}{2}$	$J_z = -\tfrac{3}{2}$
$\tfrac{3}{2}$	1	A_{111}	A_{114}	A_{144}	A_{444}
$\tfrac{1}{2}$	1	A_{112}	A_{124}, A_{115}	A_{145}, A_{244}	A_{445}
$-\tfrac{1}{2}$	1	A_{122}	A_{125}, A_{224}	A_{245}, A_{153}	A_{455}
$-\tfrac{3}{2}$	1	A_{222}	A_{225}	A_{255}	A_{555}
1	0	A_{113}	A_{134}, A_{116}	A_{146}, A_{344}	A_{446}
0	0	A_{123}	$A_{234}, A_{135}, A_{126}$	$A_{156}, A_{246}, A_{345}$	A_{456}
-1	0	A_{223}	A_{235}, A_{226}	A_{256}, A_{355}	A_{556}
$\tfrac{1}{2}$	-1	A_{133}	A_{334}, A_{136}	A_{166}, A_{346}	A_{466}
$-\tfrac{1}{2}$	-1	A_{233}	A_{335}, A_{236}	A_{266}, A_{356}	A_{566}
0	-2	A_{333}	A_{336}	A_{366}	A_{666}

(c) Operate on the $J_z = \tfrac{3}{2}$ states with $J -$ and on the $J_z = -\tfrac{3}{2}$ states with $J +$. This yields the members of the decuplet with $J_z = \tfrac{1}{2}, -\tfrac{1}{2}$. Next use I^2, J^2 to find a member of the octet and proceed similarly with stepping operators.

(d) Tabulate the results from (c).

BIBLIOGRAPHY

BAIRD, J. K., MILLER, P. D., DRESS, W. B., and RAMSAY, N. F. (1969) *Phys. Rev.* **179**, 1285.

BELL, J. S., and STEINBERGER, J. (1966) *Proceedings of the Oxford international conference on elementary particles*. RHEL.

BERNSTEIN, J., FEINBERG, G., and LEE, T. D. (1965) *Phys. Rev.* **139**, B1650.

BRENE, N., and HELLESEN, B. (1965) *Lectures on the application of unitary groups in particle physics*. NORDITA.

BRINK, D. M., and SATCHLER, G. R. (1968) *Angular momentum* (2nd edn). Clarendon Press, Oxford.

CAIRNS, I., McCUSKER, C. B. A., PEAK, L. S., and WOOLCOTT, R. L. S. (1969) *Phys. Rev.* **186**, 1394 .

CENCE, R. J., JONES, B. D., PETERSON, V. Z., STENGER, V. G., WILSON, J., CHENG, D., EANDI, R. D., KENNEY, R. W., LINSCOTT, I., OLIVER, W. P., PARKER, S., and REY, C. (1969) *Phys. Rev. Lett.* **22**, 1210.

CHRISTENSON, J. H., CRONIN, J. W., FITCH, V. L., and TURLAY, R. (1964) *Phys. Rev. Lett.* **13**, 138.

COLEMAN, S., and GLASHOW, S. L. (1961) *Phys. Rev. Lett.* **6**, 423.

CONDON, E. U., and SHORTLEY, G. H. (1935) *The theory of atomic spectra*. Cambridge University Press.

COSTA, G., and KABIR, P. K. (1967) *Phys. Rev. Lett.* **18**, 429.

CULLIGAN, G., FRANK, S. G. F., and HOLT, J. R. (1959) *Proc. phys. Soc. Lond.* **73**, 169.

DANBY, G., GAILLARD, J. M., GOULIANOS, K., LEDERMAN, L. M., MISTRY, N., SCHWARTZ, M., and STEINBERGER, J. (1962) *Phys. Rev. Lett.* **9**, 36.

DE SWART, J. J. (1963) *Rev. mod. Phys.* **35**, 916.

DE SWART, J. J. (1964) *SU₃ Symmetry and particle physics*. NIRNS.

DE SWART, J. J. (1966) *Proceedings of the 1966 CERN school of physics*. CERN 66-29.

DUCLOS, J., FREYTAG, D., SCHLÜPMANN, K., SOERGEL, V., HEINTZE, J., and RIESEBERG, H. (1965) *Phys. Lett.* **19**, 253.

EDMONDS, A. R. (1957) *Angular momentum in quantum mechanics*. Princeton University Press.

EMMERSON, J. McL., and QUIRK, T. W. (1969) *Phys. Rev. Lett.* **23**, 393.

FELD, B. J. (1967) *The quark model of the elementary particles*. CERN 67-21.

FITCH, V. L. (1967) *Proceedings of the XIIIth international conference on high energy physics, Berkeley*.

GELL–MANN, M., and NE'EMAN, Y. (1964) *The eightfold way*. Benjamin.

GOLDHABER, M., GRODZINS, L., and SUNYAR, A. W. (1958) *Phys. Rev.* **109**, 1015.

GORMLEY, M., HYMAN, E., LEE, W., NASH, T., PEOPLES, J., SCHULTZ, C., and STEIN, S. (1968) *Phys. Rev. Lett.* **21**, 402.

KÄLLEN, G. (1964) *Elementary particle physics*. Addison Wesley.

KABIR, P. K. (1968) *The CP puzzle, strange decays of the neutral kaon*. Academic Press.

KIRÁLY, P., and WOLFENDALE, A. W. (1970) *Phys. Lett.* **31B**, 410.

LEE, T. D. (1966) *Proceedings of the Oxford international conference on elementary particles*. RHEL.

MARGENAU, H., and MURPHY, G. M. (1961) *The mathematics of physics and chemistry* (2nd edn). Van Nostand.

MASSAM, T. (1968) *The quark hunters' progress.* CERN 68-24.

McCUSKER, C. B. A., and CAIRNS, I. (1969) *Phys. Rev. Lett.* **23**, 658.

McNAMEE, P., and CHILTON, F. (1964) *Rev. mod. Phys.* **36**, 1005.

NILSSON, J. (1967) *Proceedings of the 1967 CERN school of physics.* CERN 67-24,

RITTENBERG, A., BARBARO–GALTIERI, A., LASINSKI, T., ROSENFELD, A. H., TRIPPE, T. G., ROOS, M., BRICMAN, C., SÖDING, P., BARASCH–SCHMIDT, N., and WOHL, C. G. (1971) *Rev. mod. Phys.* **43**, S 1.

ROSE, M. E. (1957) *Elementary theory of angular momentum.* Wiley.

SAKURAI, J. J. (1964) *Invariance principles and elementary particles.* Princeton University Press.

SPEISER, D. R. (1964) *Proceedings of the Istanbul international summer school of theoretical physics, 1962.*

THRESHER, J. J. (1971) *Proceedings of the Daresbury study weekend 29–31 January 1971.* DNPL/R9, 193.

VAN HOVE, L. (1965) *Proceedings of the 1965 CERN Easter school for physicists.* CERN 65-24.

VIVARGENT, M. (1967) *Proceedings of the 1967 CERN school of physics.* CERN 67-24.

WEYL, H. (1952) *Symmetry.* Princeton University Press.

WICK, G. C., WIGHTMAN, A. S., and WIGNER, E. P. (1952) *Phys. Rev.* **88**, 101.

WIGNER, E. P. (1959) *Group theory and its application to the quantum mechanics of atomic spectra.* Academic Press.

WIGNER, E. P. (1967) *Symmetries and reflections.* Indiana University Press.

WOLFENSTEIN, L. (1964) *Phys. Rev. Lett.* **13**, 562.

WU, C. S., AMBLER, E., HAYWARD, R. W., HOPPES, D. D., and HUDSON, R. P. (1957) *Phys. Rev.* **105**, 1413.

INDEX